PHILOSOPHICAL PROBLEMS IN LOGIC

SYNTHESE LIBRARY

MONOGRAPHS ON EPISTEMOLOGY,

LOGIC, METHODOLOGY, PHILOSOPHY OF SCIENCE,

SOCIOLOGY OF SCIENCE AND OF KNOWLEDGE,

AND ON THE MATHEMATICAL METHODS OF

SOCIAL AND BEHAVIORAL SCIENCES

HUMANITIES PRESS / NEW YORK

PHILOSOPHICAL PROBLEMS IN LOGIC

Some Recent Developments

edited by

KAREL LAMBERT
University of California, Irvine

D. REIDEL PUBLISHING COMPANY / DORDRECHT-HOLLAND

SOLE DISTRIBUTORS FOR U.S.A. AND CANADA
HUMANITIES PRESS / NEW YORK

SBN Number: 391-00103-5

Printed in The Netherlands by D. Reidel, Dordrecht

PREFACE

The essays in this volume are based on addresses presented during a colloquium on free logic, modal logic and related areas held at the University of California at Irvine, in May of 1968. With the single exception of Dagfinn Føllesdal, whose revised address is included in a recent issue of *Synthese* honoring W. V. Quine, all of the speakers at the Irvine colloquium are contributors to this volume. Thanks are due to Professor A. I. Melden, Chairman of the Department of Philosophy at Irvine, for his enthusiastic support of the colloquium, and to Drs. Gordon Brittan and Daniel Dennett for their help in the administration of the colloquium. Finally, I should also like to thank Professor Ralph W. Gerard, Dean of the Graduate Division of the University of California at Irvine, for the financial support which made the colloquium possible.

KAREL LAMBERT

Laguna Beach, California, 1969

TABLE OF CONTENTS

KAREL LAMBERT AND BAS C. VAN FRAASSEN

MEANING RELATIONS, POSSIBLE OBJECTS, AND POSSIBLE WORLDS*

Our aims are threefold. First we shall present our philosophical approach to meaning and modality, and outline the formal semantics which it provides for modal logics (Sections I and II). Secondly, we shall show that for certain philosophical reasoning concerning truths *ex vi terminorum*, the logic of possible objects provides an explication where the logic of modal operators does not (Section III). Finally, we shall explore the extension of our theory to names and definite descriptions (Section IV).

I. INTRODUCTION

In the intricate and often confusing theory of terms developed in traditional logic, various semantic relations among predicates (general terms) were distinguished. For example, the tradition distinguishes between a predicate being *extensionally included* and being *intensionally included* in another. These metalinguistic relations had object language counterparts; thus **F** is extensionally included in **G** exactly when 'All (actual) individuals which are F are G' is true, and **F** is intensionally included in **G** if 'Necessarily, all individuals which are F are G' is true.

This use of the term 'necessarily' – to signal intensional relations among predicates – seems to have loomed large in the traditional logic of the modalities. (Consider, for example, such typical remarks as the modal qualifier "says how the predicate inheres in the subject" (William of Sherwood) or "concerns only the value of the copula" (Kant).) On this use, however, iterations of modal qualifiers would seem to have no point. Thus consider another object language counterpart of the metalinguistic assertion that **F** is intensionally included in **G**: All (possible) individuals which are F are G. Symbolizing the two counterparts as $\Box(Fx \supset Gx)$ and $(/x)(Fx \supset Gx)$ respectively, it would seem that $\Box\Box(Fx \supset Gx)$ corresponds to $(/x)(/x)(Fx \supset Gx)$, a case of vacuous quantification. Thus, if $\Box\Box$ makes sense here, it reduces to $\Box$, and $\Box\Diamond$ reduces to $\Box$, and so on. Hereafter, we shall call this use the *quantificational* use of modal qualifiers,

K. Lambert (ed.), Philosophical Problems in Logic.

because of the possibility of paraphrase into the 'For all possible individuals...' terminology.

The use of modal qualifiers to signal intensional *meaning* relations has important consequences (as will be seen in Section III); but it is better served by the 'possible individuals' quantifier than by a modal operator. For example, a tenacious and widely held opinion, advocated most vigorously in this century by C. I. Lewis,[1] was that the valid laws governing intensional meaning relations are exactly those governing relations of extension. Lewis' opinion was recently resurrected by Henry Leonard[2] who argued that the laws governing the 'possible individuals' quantifier are exactly those of standard quantification theory. The main problem before us at this point is that of providing a semantics for this 'unrestricted' quantifier, one which will allow us to make sense of possible individuals discourse without involvement in objectionable metaphysical commitments.

In MRP such a semantics was given, following an idea from Wittgenstein's *Tractatus*. Associated with the language is a *logical space* in which each individual in the domain of discourse has a location. Each predicate is assigned a region of logical space, and a point in logical space satisfies the formula **Fx** if it lies in the region assigned to **F**. Now 'For all possible *x*, *Fx*' is true if **Fx** is satisfied by all points in this space, and 'For all actual *x*, *Fx*' is true if **Fx** is satisfied by all those points which are occupied by members of the domain of discourse. The English sentence 'All possible scarlet things are red' is true, because the region of the relevant logical space (the color spectrum) assigned to 'scarlet' is part of the region assigned to 'red'.

We now consider other functions of modal qualifiers, which cannot be accommodated within the above scheme, and for which iteration is neither senseless nor vacuous. We shall discuss two varieties, a kind of physical modality and a kind of strict or logical modality. We shall do this by means of an example: suppose that our language is designed to formulate descriptions of some physical system X (a computer, a rigid body, a switch, a muscle, an atom). Let X have a state-space H; this means that H is a mathematical space whose points represent the various states that X can have. (If X is a two-position switch, H may be $\{0, 1\}$ with 0 representing the 'off' position and 1 the 'on' position.) For each property F, we know the region $H(F)$ such that X has F if and only if X is in a state represented by a point in region $H(F)$. Now our theory may provide for certain kinds of changes in the state of X; or rather, it may limit the set of possible such changes. For example, it may say that if X is in state s_1, then it will evolve into a state in region R; this precludes finding X first in state s_1 and then in a state outside R. So there is a set of transformations U_t^i of H such that the theory does not preclude transition from a state s to state $U_t^i(s)$ over a time-interval of length t. These form the set **U** of *physically possible transitions.* And now we may give as truth-conditions for modal statements:

> 'Necessarily, X is F' is true in state s if and only if $U(s)$ is in region $H(F)$ for every member U of **U**.

The composition of the set **U** will now determine what laws govern the iteration of modal operators.

Considering for a moment the example of the simple two-position switch X, note that 'Necessarily X is on or X is off' will be a valid sentence. But if we meant the modal qualifier not in the sense of physical modality, but in the sense of logical modality, this would be incorrect. For of course, *X could* be in a third position, namely if it were rebuilt into a three-position switch (or if it had been a three-position switch to begin). Here we are envisaging changes in the *structure* of logical space.

Generalizing, we may say that modal operators concern (in a certain sense to be explicated) transformations of logical space. And we may distinguish between two general modes of modality: *natural modality* in which these transformations amount only to actual individuals changing location in the space (or coming into being, or being destroyed), and *strict modality* in which these transformations affect the structure of logical space. In the former case, logical space gives the general form of any possible world; in the latter case, other possible worlds may not partake of this general form.[3] In other words, the concept of 'logical space' is adequate to the representation of a certain kind of possible world (i.e., natural) but not to an enlarged notion of possible world.

Elsewhere we have explored the mathematical representation of both modes of modality at once; in this essay we shall limit ourselves to the case of strict modality.[4]

II. POSSIBLE OBJECTS AND MODAL OPERATORS

We shall discuss first the logic of possible objects, interpreted as above, without modal operators; then we shall introduce such operators. In MRP we defined a class $C(S)$ of languages with syntax S, called *semi-interpreted languages*. The primitive logical symbols of $C(S)$ are $=$, $\sim$, &,), (, /, and we read $(/x)\,A$ as 'For all possible objects x, A'. The ordinary quantifier (x), read as 'For all actual objects x', is defined contextually by $(x)\,A \equiv (/x)\,(E!x \supset A)$, where $E!$ ('exists') is a special monadic predicate constant.

When L is a member of $C(S)$ it has besides this syntax associated with it a non-empty set H and a mapping f of the n-ary predicates (other than $E!, =$) into subsets of H^n (the set of n-tuples of members of H). The function f is called the *interpretation function*. Strictly speaking, the logical space of L should be identified with the couple $\langle H, \{f(P): P \text{ a predicate}\}\rangle$, but we also use 'logical space' loosely to refer to set H. To change the structure of the logical space means to change the function f, and/or to enlarge or narrow H.

A model for L is any couple $M = \langle loc, D\rangle$, where D is a set and *loc* a one-one mapping of D into H. D is the domain of discourse, and each member of D thus has a location in logical space. The truth-definition for L is quite straightforward; for the sake of later convenience, we shall here use the term *satisfaction*. We use d, with or without accents or subscripts, to range over H^ω (the set of denumerable sequences of members of H), and write $d\,(x)$ for the *ith* member of d when x is the *ith* variable of L. We write 'd satisfies A in model M' as $M \Vdash A\,[d]$, and 'iff' for 'if and only if'.

(1)	$M \Vdash (E!x)\,[d]$	iff	$d(x) = \text{loc}(b)$ for some b in D, where $\text{M} = \langle loc, \text{D}\rangle$.
(2)	$M \Vdash (P^n x_1 \dots x_n)\,[d]$	iff	$\langle d\,(x_1), \dots, d(x_n)\rangle \in f\,(P^n)$
(3)	$M \Vdash (x = y)\,[d]$	iff	$d(x) = d(y)$
(4)	$M \Vdash (\sim A)\,[d]$	iff	not $M \Vdash A[d]$
(5)	$M \Vdash (A\ \&\ B)\,[d]$	iff	$M \Vdash A\,[d]$ and $M \Vdash B\,[d]$
(6)	$M \Vdash (/x)\,A\,[d]$	iff	$M \Vdash A\,[d']$ for all d' like d except perhaps at x (briefly, $d' =_x d$).

We shall call h a *satisfaction function* for L if h is defined exactly for the sentences of L and there is a model M such that

$$h(A) = \{d \in H^\omega : M \Vdash A\,[d]\}$$

for all sentences A of L. It will be convenient henceforth to discuss logical relations in terms of satisfaction-functions. (Note that H, f, and M determine h, and that conversely, h determines H, f, and M up to isomorphism.)

We say that a sentence A is *valid* ($\Vdash A$) in L if all sequences in H^{ω} satisfy in all models; equivalently, if $h(A) = H^{\omega}$ for all satisfaction-functions h for L. And we say that $A_1, \ldots, A_n$ *semantically entail* B ($A_1, \ldots, A_n \Vdash B$) in L if B is satisfied whenever $A_1 \ldots, A_n$ are satisfied; that is, if $h(A_1) \cap \cdots \cap h(A_n)$ is included in $h(B)$, for all satisfaction-functions h for L. If X is a set of sentences, we understand $X \Vdash A$ in that way: A is satisfied whenever all members of X are satisfied. And if C is a class of languages, we say that $X \Vdash A$ in C if this is the case in every language in the class C.

It can now be proved (MRP, Section 6) that $A_1, \ldots, A_n \Vdash B$ in $C(S)$ if and only if B is derivable from $A_1, \ldots, A_n$ in classical quantificational logic (with identity and $(/x)$ as the universal quantifier). In addition, the logic of the restricted quantifier (x) is *free logic*.[5]

In the generalization in which modal operators are accommodated, the emphasis will be entirely on satisfaction functions rather than models and interpretation functions. This is merely a matter of convenience. The transformations of logical space will define correlate transformations of the satisfaction functions, and it is these to which we shall direct our attention. A few intuitive comments may facilitate the transition. When we discuss what is possible, in a semi-interpreted language, we discuss what is true when the logical space H, interpretation function f, and model M have been replaced by a new logical space H', a new interpretation function f', and a new model M'. We shall assume that we have a large set K, of which H is part, and from which H' is taken. Now H, f, and M determine a satisfaction function h such that for all sentences A, $h(A) \subseteq H^{\omega} \subseteq K^{\omega}$. Likewise, H', f', M' determine such a function h', such that for all sentences A, $h'(a) \subseteq H'^{\omega} \subseteq K^{\omega}$. We are going to study the set T of transformations which lead from h to h'.

Accordingly, we now define a class $C(S_m)$ of languages with syntax S_m. This syntax is as before, except that we add the propositional operator $\Box$. Associated with a language L in $C(S_m)$ are not only a non-empty set H and interpretation function f, but also a superset K of H, and a set T of transformations satisfying certain conditions which we shall now explain.

We denote as K^* the set of functions f defined on the sentences of L, such that $f(A) \subseteq K^{\omega}$ for any such sentence A. Each member t of T is now a transformation on K^*. For any function f in K^* we define the space of f, $Sp(f)$, to be the least set J such that

$$f(A) \subseteq J^{\omega} \text{ for all sentences } A.$$

Clearly not all the members of K^* are proper generalizations of the satisfaction-functions of the preceding section. We call a member h of K^* a *satisfaction-function* for L (in $C(S_m)$) iff the following conditions are satisfied:

(1′) There is a subset $h(E!)$ of $Sp(h)$ such that $h(E!x) = \{d \in Sp(h)^{\omega} : d(x) \in h(E!)\}$

(2′) There is for each predicate P of degree n a subset $h(P)$ of $Sp(h)^n$ such that $h(Px_1 \ldots x_n) = \{d \in Sp(h)^{\omega} : \langle d(x_1), \ldots, d(x_n) \rangle \in h(P)\}$

(3′) $h(x = y) = \{d \in Sp(h)^{\omega} : d(x) = d(y)\}$

(4′) $h(\sim A) = Sp(h)^{\omega} - h(A)$

(5′) $h(A \;\&\; B) = h(A) \cap h(B)$

(6′) $h((/x)A) = \{d \in Sp(h)^{\omega} : d' \in h(A) \text{ for all } d' =_x d \text{ in } Sp(h)^{\omega}\}$

(7′) $h(\Box A) = \{d \in Sp(h)^{\omega} : d \in th(A) \text{ for all } t \in T\}$

If h is furthermore such that $Sp(h) = H$ and $h(P) = f(P)$ for each predicate P, we shall call h a *principal satisfaction function* for L.

We have two ways of generalizing validity in L; we may call A valid in L iff $h(A) = Sp(h)^{\omega}$ for all principal satisfaction functions, or for all satisfaction functions. In the former case we would expect that there are sentences A such that $\Vdash A$ but not $\Vdash \Box A$, even if all desirable conditions are fulfilled: A would be intraconceptually (naturally), but not extra-conceptually (strictly), necessary. Henceforth we shall mean 'valid' in the second sense; and similarly we shall say that $A_1, \ldots, A_n \Vdash B$ in L iff $h(A_1) \cap \cdots \cap h(A_n) \subseteq h(B)$ for all satisfaction functions h for L. Finally, we shall say again that these relations hold in a class $\mathbf{C}$ of languages in $C(S_m)$ iff they hold in all members of $\mathbf{C}$.

For greater definiteness, we shall henceforth identify L with the quintuple $\langle S_m, H, f, K, T \rangle$. From the point of view of logic the laws which hold in a specific language of the kind in question are not usually of much interest; one would rather consider those which hold in a class of such languages, a class characterized by some interesting set of assumptions about their structure.

We shall now introduce a number of assumptions concerning the set T of transformations, and note how they (cumulatively) entail the validity of certain well-known principles of modal logic. (For proofs we refer to MRM.)

ASSUMPTION 1. If f is a satisfaction function, so is $t(f)$, for all t in T. This rules out, for example, that $\Diamond(A \& {\sim} A)$ might be true (Henceforth we write 'tf' for '$t(f)$', and so forth.)

ASSUMPTION 2. $Sp(h) \subseteq Sp(th)$, for all satisfaction functions h, and all t in T.

Now we can prove that if $\Vdash A$ then $\Vdash \Box A$, and that $\Box A, \Box(A \supset B) \Vdash \Box B$.

ASSUMPTION 3. T contains an *identity element*, that is, a member i such that $if = f$ for all f in K^*.

From this it follows that $\Box A \Vdash A$. These results correspond to the basic laws of von Wright's system M. To obtain similar results for S_4 and S_5, we add assumptions that make T respectively a *semigroup* and a *group*.

ASSUMPTION 4. For all t, t' in T, the composition tt' is in T.

It now follows that $\Box A \Vdash \Box\Box A$.

ASSUMPTION 5. For all t in T, T contains an inverse, that is, an element t^* such that $t^*t = i$.

If $\Diamond$ is defined as usual, then we can now prove the 'Brouwersche axiom', $A \Vdash \Box\Diamond A$.

In quantified modal logic, the best known principles are the *Barcan Principle* and its converse:

$$(x)\Box A \supset \Box(x) A \quad BP$$
$$\Box(x) A \supset (x)\Box A \quad (Cv\ \mathrm{BP})$$

These are now usually argued not to hold in general.[6] For example, the second has the consequence $(x)\Box E!x$: every actual existent exists necessarily. It is easy to see that these principles do not follow, in our framework, unless special assumptions are made relating $th(E!x)$ to $h(E!x)$.

But it is not so implausible to have the analogues of these principles for the unrestricted quantifier $(/x)$ hold. Assumptions 1 and 2 suffice to prove that $\Box(/x) A \Vdash (/x)\Box A$. The analogue to the Barcan principle, $(/x)\Box A \Vdash \Box(/x) A$, follows from:

ASSUMPTION 6. $Sp(th) \subseteq Sp(h)$, for all t in T and all satisfaction-functions h.

Now the principle $(/x) \Box A \Vdash \Box (/x) A$ holds.

It may be noted that these assumptions are not the only ones that lead to the results noted. For example, Assumption 3 could be replaced by the assumption that for each h in K^*, there is a member t of T such that $t(h) = h$. But in that case an identity element could be added to T without changing the set of valid arguments, so that there is no loss in the more elegant assumption which we actually made.

The usual completeness proofs for modal logics can rather easily be adapted to our present scheme; in the appendix this is done in detail for Thomason's system S_4Q_1, an S_4-type system of quantificational modal logic.

III. POSSIBLE OBJECTS, POSSIBLE WORLDS, AND TRUTHS EX VI TERMINORUM

In the two preceding sections we distinguished between two uses of the word 'necessarily'. In some cases, it seems to have a purely quantificational use. For instance, 'Necessarily, all scarlet things are red' appears to signify the intensional inclusion of 'scarlet' in 'red', and we have suggested that the formulation of the material mode might better proceed by means of the 'all possibles' quantifier: 'All possible scarlet things are red'. In this section, we seek to bolster that opinion by means of a specific example. Briefly, we shall show that an argument developed by Hilary Putnam and Arthur Pap[7] to the effect that 'Nothing can be both red and green all over' (at once) is true *ex vi terminorum* is not valid when construed as modal talk, but is valid when construed as an argument about possible objects. To show the invalidity of the former interpretation, we shall give a counter-example in the usual (Kripke-style) semantics. (A similar example in our own semantics is given equally easily, but might be thought to prejudice the matter.)

Just over a decade ago, Hilary Putnam tried to show that the statement 'Nothing is both red and green all over' is true by virtue of the meanings of words alone. Where 'E' is shorthand for the relational expression 'having the same color as', his premises were (essentially) the following.

P1. $(x)(y)(z)(Exx \mathbin{\&} (Exy \mathbin{\&} Eyz \cdot \supset Eyx \mathbin{\&} Exz))$

P2. F is a color $\equiv (\exists y)(x)(Fx \equiv Exy)$

Here Premise P1 shows that Putnam's relation E (has the same color as) is an equivalence relation, and Premise P2 is essentially what Putnam proposed as the definition of 'is a color'. From this pair of premises he deduced the (L-true) statement

3. $(F \text{ is a color} \;\&\; G \text{ is a color} \;\&\; F \neq G) \supset (x) \sim (Fx \;\&\; Gx)$

which says that if F and G are distinct colors, nothing is both F and G all over. But there is a problem here about the meaning of 'distinct': what does the conjunct $F \neq G$ in the antecedent of 3 signify? The main candidate seems to be:

C. $\sim (x)\,(Fx \equiv Gx)$

If C is chosen as the meaning of $F \neq G$, Putnam's argument *is* valid. But then it defeats his purpose, which is to show that 'Nothing is both red and green all over' is true *ex vi terminorum*. For C cannot be true on linguistic grounds alone, since it implies the contingent truth that there exists something which is either F or G (something red or something green, in this case).

For reasons apparently of this sort, Pap proposed a non-metalinguistic reformulation of Putnam's argument in essentially quantified modal ($S5$) logic. He replaced P2 and C by

P2*. $F \text{ is a color} \equiv (\exists y)\,(x)\,\Box(Fx \equiv Eyx)$
C*. $F \neq G \equiv \sim (x)\,\Box(Fx \equiv Gx)$.

Subsequently Putnam suggested a further alteration of P^{2*}, presumably to cover Hume's 'missing shade of blue':

P2**. $F \text{ is a color} \equiv \Box((\exists y)\,(Fy) \supset (\exists y)\,(x)\,(Fx \equiv Eyx))$.

In either case, however, the argument to Conclusion 3 is invalid.[8]

Following the terminology of Kripke's paper[9] on $S5$, let $M = \langle \alpha, \{\alpha, \beta\} \rangle$ be a model with principal world α and possible worlds α and β. Let the domain of M be $D = \{a, b, c\}$ and let the assignments of extensions to F, E and G in α and β be:

$$\alpha(F) = \alpha(G) = D \quad \beta(F) = \{a, c\} \quad \beta(G) = \{b\}$$
$$\alpha(E) = D^2 \quad \beta(E) = \{\langle a, a\rangle, \langle b, b\rangle, \langle c, c\rangle, \langle a, c\rangle, \langle c, a\rangle\}$$

We note the following:

(A) E is an equivalence relation in D in both α and β
(B) $(x)\Box(Fx \equiv Eax)$ is valid in M
(C) $(x)\Box(Gx \equiv Ebx)$ is valid in M

Together, (A)–(C) establish that F and G are colors in M, by either P^{2*} or P_2^{**}. But we also note that

(D) In β, $\sim(Fc \equiv Gc)$ is true; therefore
$\sim(x)\Box(Fx \equiv Gx)$ is true in α
(E) In α, $(x)\sim(Fx \,\&\, Gx)$ is false

Thus in α, F and G are distinct colors and yet something has both F and G. This shows that the argument is not valid in quantified $S5$ (and hence not in the weaker M, B, or $S4$).

Still, the Putnam-Pap argument has great intuitive force. That F and G are distinct colors means only that some possible object does not have both. But then, just in virtue of their being colors, it would seem to follow that no possible object has both. However this assumes that the relation of having the same color is an equivalence relation on *possible* objects. And Putnam and Pap had no formal way of formulating this. Since we now have a logic of possible objects at our disposal, we can reconstrue the intuitive argument above in such a way that it becomes valid. We do this by rendering E as an 'equivalence relation on the possible individuals' (that is, as an equivalence relation on logical space), and colors as E-equivalence classes.

P_1'. $(/x)(/y)(/x)(Exx \,\&\, (Exy \,\&\, Eyz \cdot \supset Eyx \,\&\, Eyz))$
P_2'. $(/\exists x)(/y)(Fy \equiv Exy)$
P_3'. $(/\exists x)(/y)(Gy \equiv Exy)$
P_4'. $\sim(/y)(Fy \equiv Gy)$

The conclusion of the Putnam-Pap argument is now formulated as

$$(y)\sim(Fy \,\&\, Gy))$$

that is, no actual object is both red and green all over.

The proof of the validity of this argument is a simple exercise in standard quantification theory. For it will be recalled that the above conclusion is definitionally equivalent to

$$(/y)\,(E!y \supset \sim (Fy \;\&\; Gy))$$

and that standard quantificational inference is sound for the 'all possibles' quantifier.

IV. POSSIBLE OBJECTS, VIRTUAL OBJECTS, AND SINGULAR TERMS

We have so far considered no singular terms except variables, and this rather restricts our means of expression. For we have of course as a theorem

$$(/\exists x)\,(x = y)$$

(which we shall render briefly as $S!y$, 'y is a possible object' or 'y subsists') so that a variable can presumably not stand for, say, 'the round square of Phineas'. There may be some latitude in what is to count as a possible object, but round squares seem definitely beyond the pale. We can find even worse examples; thus of 'the square of Phineas which is both round and not round' we would presumably wish to say that it is not even *possibly* a possible object. The distinction between these two cases is the following: we may admit as conceivable sufficient changes in the structure of the language to render 'There are round squares' no longer false *ex vi terminorum*. But if we make Assumption 1 of Section II – as we shall here – we cannot say the same for 'Some round things are not round.'

So we find that there are two kinds of individuals which are not possible individuals. The former are possibly possible individuals, and the latter are not. We should like to have singular terms **a**, **b** in our language which can be used to 'refer' to such entities, so that both

$$\sim (/\exists y)\,(y = \mathbf{a}) \;\&\; \Diamond\,(/\exists y)\,(y = \mathbf{a})$$

and

$$\sim (/\exists y)\,(y = \mathbf{b}) \;\&\; \sim \Diamond\,(/\exists y)\,(y = \mathbf{b})$$

may be true. (If we do not make Assumption 4 of Section II, the latter is consistent with $\Diamond\Diamond\,(/\exists y)\,(y = \mathbf{b})$ as well as with $\sim\Diamond\Diamond\,(/\exists y)\,(y = \mathbf{b})$, and so on, so that then a further subdivision may be made. But we shall here make Assumption 4 for simplicity's sake.)

It is clear that **a** and **b** cannot be variables here; their 'referents' do not lie within the range of our quantifiers. (That is, $(/x)A \,\&\, S!\mathbf{a} \Vdash (\mathbf{a}/x)A$ but not $(/x)A \Vdash (\mathbf{a}/x)A$.) This is reminiscent of Scott's *virtuals* and *impossibles*. We shall use these terms (**a** is a virtual object and **b** an impossible object) although our interpretation is different from his. One reason for so doing is that the examples of virtual objects that are given appear to fit the above classification. For example, Quine's virtual classes are the kind of object which we might postulate to exist in some set theory (not all in the same set theory, of course). And the perfect frictionless plane, or perpetuum mobile, may be the kind of thing which we cannot conceive of as existing, given our present scientific background-theories, but which we might agree a conceptual revolution in science might make a possible object.

Before looking at the semantics of these terms, we must point to another distinction, which has been explored by R. H. Thomason.[10] This is the distinction between *substances* and *accidents*. Roughly following his usage we shall say that a term **c** 'refers' to a *substance* if

$$(/\exists x)\Box(x=\mathbf{c})$$

is true. It is clear from our semantics that variables 'refer' to substances, because we have

$$x=y \Vdash \Box(x=y)$$

holding for L in $C(S_m)$. We shall now provide intuitive ground for not wishing this to hold for all singular terms.

Consider the old question: 'How many legs does an ass have if we call its tail a leg?' The edifying answer is 'Four; because calling a tail a leg does not make it a leg.' But suppose we give this dialogue a different cast: let interlocutor and respondent agree at time t that henceforth the tail shall be called a leg, and let the interlocutor ask at a later time t': 'How many legs does an ass have?'. The respondent's correct answer is now 'Five'; and indeed, the respondent must now say 'There does not exist such a thing as the tail of the ass; however, there is something which is a leg but which did not use to be a leg' – provided, of course, that by 'x did not use to be a leg' he means that the sentence 'x is a leg' used to be false. This shows at once the need for singular terms in our language whose 'referents' remain the same throughout meaning change, and for singular terms whose 'referents' depend on meaning relations in the language. Our variables play the former role; definite descriptions such as 'the tail of the ass' in our story (or 'the mass of the body' in the transition from classical to relativistic physics) play the latter role. Names seem to vary in this (see Thomason, *loc. cit*), so we shall put no restrictions on them in this respect. This means that they are rather more like descriptions than like variables, but it might be contingently the case that they 'refer' to a substance.

There is a further distinction between names and descriptions: the latter describe their referents (if any), and this validates certain inferences. We shall write '$(\mathrm{I}x)A$' for 'the one and only possible individual such that A' and '$(\iota x)A$' for 'the one and only actual individual such that A', the latter being defined by

D0. $(\iota x)A = (Ix)\,(E!x\ \&\ A).$

The intended meaning requires therefore the following basic principles

D1. $(/y)\,(y = (Ix)A \equiv .\ \ (y/x)A\ \&\ (/x)\ A \supset x = y))$
D2. $(y)\,(y = (\iota x)A \equiv E!y\ \&\ (y/x)A\ \&\ (x)\,(A \supset x = y)),$

where x and y are distinct variables. Here D1 has D2 as consequence, and even the stronger.

D2′. $(/y)\,(y = (\iota x)A \equiv E!y\ \&\ (y/x)A\ \ \&\ \ (x)\,(A \supset x = y)).$

Thus our semantics must be such that D1 is valid. This is the minimal criterion for an adequate theory of descriptions. One might consider the acceptance of stronger conditions, such as the identification of impossibles, or even the identification of impossibles *and* virtuals, or the condition that $\mathbf{a} = (Ix)\,(x = \mathbf{a})$ even when $\mathbf{a}$ is a virtual or impossible object. But we shall not linger over these.[11]

There are, as we now know, a number of alternative approaches to the semantics of singular terms. We shall here follow the approach which we developed in previous papers,[12] which is to leave the referent (or 'referent') of a singular term undefined when it does not exist (or 'subsist'). Thus in the scheme of MRP, an interpretation function f will now assign to *some* constants and *some* descriptions a point in logical space. When the description has free variables in it, it may be assigned such a point relative to some assignments of values to the variables in H. When nothing is thus assigned to a singular term $\mathbf{a}$, there will nevertheless be conditions governing the truth-conditions of a sentence $A(\mathbf{a})$ in which $\mathbf{a}$ occurs, designed to preserve sentential logic, self-identity, and the indiscernibility of identicals. Given our previous work, it would be a matter of relatively routine work to do this for the class of languages $C(S)$ discussed in MRP (see Section II above). For the class of languages $C(S_m)$, the same can be done by placing the following additional clauses in the definition of 'satisfaction function h for language L in $C(S_m)$' in Section II:

(8′) $h(\mathbf{a}=\mathbf{a}) = Sp(h)^{\omega}$

(9′) $h(\mathbf{a}=\mathbf{b}\ \&\ A) \subseteq h((\mathbf{b}/\mathbf{a})A)$

(10′) if $d(x) = d'(x)$ for all x occurring in A, then $d \in h(A)$ iff $d' \in h(A)$

(11′) For all α in $Sp(h)$, if for all $d' =_x d$, $d' \in h(A)$ iff $d'(x) = \alpha$, then $d \in h(((Ix)A/y)B)$ iff $f'' \in h(B)$ where $d'' =_y d$, $d''(y) = \alpha$; and if no member α of $Sp(h)$ is thus, $d \in h((/y)(y \neq (Ix)A))$

where $\mathbf{a}$, $\mathbf{b}$ are arbitrary singular terms (variables, names, descriptions). By these restrictions, we ensure that classical propositional logic and free quantification theory ($\Vdash (/x)A \,\&\, S!\mathbf{b}. \supset (\mathbf{b}/x)A$), as well as the minimal description theory codified in D1, hold.

There is one further problem which we wish to consider, and to handle it we shall have to extend the language still further. It seems to us that there is reason to desire quantification 'over' virtuals and even 'over' impossibles. (We shall use 'individual' as the most generic term, so that possibles, virtuals, and impossibles are all individuals.) For example, the inference from 'John believes in the Supreme Being' to 'John believes in something' seems impeccable – and its acceptance does not seem to prejudge the question whether the Supreme Being is even possibly a possible entity. But secondly, it also seems to us that individuals which are not possibles have only a most ethereal mode of being, the mode of being merely a subject for discourse. This distinction will be honored in our construction.

We have not assigned points in logical space (or any superset thereof) to terms 'referring to' virtual objects, so that quantification 'over' virtuals must be handled in a new way. There is in fact a rather painless way to introduce such quantification, – with the help of the substitution interpretation of the quantifiers which has been explored by Beth, Marcus, Dunn and Belnap, Leblanc and others.[14] To do this, we enlarge the set of sentences of L by adding a new quantifier Q, and stipulating that if A is a sentence so is $(Qx)A$, and that the new set of sentences is again closed under $\sim$, &, $\Box$, and $(/x)$. (To simplify matters we shall not add to the singular terms; thus Q does not occur in any definite description.) The new language will be called L_q, and it will have as admissible valuations a set V_q defined below. Assume that $L = \langle S_m, H, f, K, T \rangle$ and the syntax of L_q is formed as indicated.

The set V_q of admissible valuations of L_q is the set of all mappings v of the sentences of L_q into $\{T, F\}$ for which there is a satisfaction function h for L and sequence d in $Sp(h)$ – we say that *v reduces to h and d* – such that:

(i) if A is a sentence of L then $v(A) = T$ iff $d \in h(A)$
(ii) if A is not a sentence of L, $v(A)$ is defined inductively:

(a) $v(\sim A) = T$ iff $v(A) = F$
(b) $v(A \,\&\, B) = T$ iff $v(A) = v(B) = T$
(c) $v((Qx)A) = T$ iff $v((\mathbf{b}/x)A) = T$ for every singular term **b**
(d) $v((/x)A) = T$ iff for every $d' =_x d$ in $Sp(h)$ and every v', if v' reduces to h and d' then $v'(A) = T$
(e) $v(\Box A) = T$ iff for every t in T and every v', if v' reduces to th and d then $v'(A) = T$.

A very inclusive kind of quantification can now be defined à la Leonard[15] contextually as

$$[x]A \equiv (/x)A \,\&\, (Qx)A$$

where $[x]$ may be read as 'For all individuals'. Using '$V!\mathbf{b}$', read as 'b is a virtual', as abbreviation for '$\Diamond S!\mathbf{b}$', we may define quantification over virtuals contextually by

$$(vx)A \equiv [x](V!x \supset A)$$

where '(vx)' may be read as 'For all virtuals'. (Qx) is a standard substitution quantifier (see e.g. Leblanc, *op. cit.*) so that $(Qx)A \supset (t/x)A$ is valid. For the infinite case we must add

$$\{(b/x)A : \mathbf{b} \text{ a singular term}\} \Vdash (Qx)A$$

which holds, given our previous understanding of semantic entailment.

APPENDIX. TWO SYSTEMS OF MODAL QUANTIFICATION THEORY

We shall here discuss the completeness proofs within our framework, of Thomason's S_4Q_1 and S_4Q_3.[16]

Our aim will be to show that the theorems of S_4Q_1 are exactly the sentences valid in a certain class **C** of languages in $C(S_m)$ – with $(/x)$ as the universal quantifier; then we shall also relate S_4Q_3 to this class of languages. The class **C** is chosen as follows: a member L of $C(S_m)$ is a member of **C** if and only if the assumptions below are satisfied.

First we assume that all the numbered assumptions of the preceding section except Assumption 5 are satisfied. (In that case, but not otherwise, Assumption 6 is independent.) Then we add the following additional assumptions.

ASSUMPTION 7. For all t in T, and all $b \in K$, $t(b)=b$.

ASSUMPTION 8. For all satisfaction functions h for L, $Sp(h)=K$.

This second assumption means that $H=K$; that is, we admit as transformations of logical space only functions which change its structure but do not decrease or increase the set of points. The quantifier $(/x)$ always ranges over the whole of K by Assumption 8. From Assumption 7 it is clear that we think of S_4Q_1 here as a system of strict modality.

To prove the soundness of S_4Q_1, we must show that if any sentence is a theorem of S_4Q_1, then it is valid in any member L of **C**. Well, all theorems of standard quantification theory with $(/x)$ as universal quantifier are valid in L, and the rule of modus ponens preserves validity in L (see Section III). Secondly, by Assumptions 1–4, the theorems of S_4 are valid in L. Thirdly, by Assumptions 5 and 6 the analogues of the Barcan Principle and its converse for $(/x)$ are valid in L. Fourthly, Assumption 7, yields that the principles

$$x=y \Vdash \Box(x=y)$$
$$x \neq y \Vdash \Box(x \neq y)$$

hold in L. Together these laws define Thomason's system S_4Q_1.

To prove (strong) completeness for the system S_4Q_1 under the present interpretation, we must show that if a sentence A is not derivable from a set of sentences X in S_4Q_1, then $X \Vdash A$ does not hold in **C**. That is, we must then exhibit a satisfaction function h for some member L of set **C** such that $h(X)$ is not included in $h(A)$ – where $h(X)$ is the intersection of all the sets $h(B)$ such that B belongs to X. This will show then that some sequence which satisfies all the premises X does not satisfy the conclusion A, and provide us with the counter-example we need.

Our strategy will here be to rely on Thomason's original semantics which has a counterpart in ours. For this purpose we exhibit Thomason's definition of *model structure.*

> An S_4Q_1 *model structure* (m.s.) is a triple $M = \langle U, R, D\rangle$, where U and D are non-empty sets and R is a binary reflexice and transitive relation on U.

We read '$\alpha R\beta$' as 'α is possible relative to β' or 'There is access from α to β'. The members of U are called possible worlds, and D is the domain of possible individuals.

An *interpretation I* over an m.s. $M = \langle U, R, D\rangle$ is a function mapping the variables into D, and yielding for every member α of U a relativized function I_α which maps the sentences into $\{T, F\}$, $E!$ into a subset of D, and each n-ary predicate into a subset of D^n, subject to the conditions:

(a)	$I_\alpha(P^n x_1 \ldots x_n) = T$	iff	$\langle I(x_1), \ldots, I(x_n)\rangle \in I_\alpha(P^n)$
(b)	$I_\alpha(x = y) = T$	iff	$I(x) = I(y)$
(c)	$I_\alpha(E!\,x) = T$	iff	$I(x) \in I_\alpha(E!)$
(d)	$I_\alpha(\sim A) = T$	iff	$I_\alpha(A) = F$
(e)	$I_\alpha(A \mathbin{\&} B) = T$	iff	$I_\alpha(A) = I_\alpha(B) = T$
(f)	$I_\alpha((/x)A) = T$	iff	$I_\alpha a/x(A) = T$ for all $a \in D$, where $I_\alpha a/x$ is like I_α except perhaps for assigning a to x
(g)	$I_\alpha(\Box A) = T$	iff	$I_\beta(A) = T$ for all β in U such that $\alpha R\beta$.

We note that the assignment to sentences is fully determined by the other assignments, and that an interpretation I restricted to the variables is a sequence $d = \langle I(x_1), I(x_2), \ldots\rangle$ in D. We shall then write $I = I_d$ or $I_\alpha = I_{\alpha d}$ when convenient. In that case $Ia/x = I'_d$ where $d' =_x d$, $d'(x) = a$. Also note that here $E!$ is essentially an arbitrary monadic predicate.

We turn now to the construction of a satisfaction function for a language in **C** which will correspond to a given interpretation I. Let $L = \langle S_m, H, f, K, T\rangle$, with the components as specified below. We take H to be identical with K; the interpretation function f will not play a specific role in the argument and need only satisfy the general conditions laid down in Section III of MRM. We define K to be the set D, where $M = \langle U, R, D \rangle$ is a model for over which I is an interpretation. The main job is the construction of T.

To begin, we single out a certain subset of K^* by the notation h^α:

$h^\alpha(A) = \{d \in K^\omega : I_{\alpha d}(A) = T\}$ for all sentences A, for each member α of U.

Secondly, for each member α of U we define a transformation t_α on $K \cup K^*$ as follows:

(i) $$t_\alpha h^\beta = \begin{cases} h^\alpha \text{ if } \beta R_\alpha, \\ h^\beta \text{ otherwise;} \end{cases}$$

(ii) if $b \in K \cup K^*$ and $b \neq h^\beta$ for any β in U, then $t_\alpha(b) = b$.

Finally, we define T to be the smallest set containing an identity element and $\{t_\alpha : \alpha \in U\}$ which is closed under composition. We note that for all members f and f' of K^*, there is a member t of T such that $f' = tf$ if and only if there is a member α of U such that $f' = t_\alpha f$. It is also easily checked that $\alpha R \beta$ iff there is a transformation t in T such that $th^\alpha = h^\beta$ – namely, t_β. So we deduce:

> For every α in U, h^α is a satisfaction-function for L, and L is a member of **C**.

This ends the proof.

In the case of S_4Q_3, $E!$ acquires significant status: the quantifier ranges, in each possible world, exactly over the entities of which $E!$ is true. Hence the quantifier of S_4Q_3 is just our (x): where $(x)A$ abbreviates $(/x)(E!x \supset A)$. This suggests the following theorem.

> The system S_4Q_3 is sound and complete for the restricted quantifier fragment of **C**.

The proof of this theorem is similar to that of the above results for S_4Q_1, and only slightly more complex.

University of California (Irvine)

Yale University and Indiana University

REFERENCES

* The research for this paper was supported in part by NSF grant GS-1566. The first two parts of this paper comprise a brief presentation of the approach to meaning and modality developed in B. van Fraassen, 'Meaning Relations Among Predicates', *Nous* **1** (1967), 161–179 (henceforth MRP), and 'Meaning Relations and Modalities', presented at the APA (Eastern) Conference, Dec. 1968 (*Nous* **3** (1969), 155–167; henceforth MRM).

[1] C. I. Lewis and C. H. Langford, *Symbolic Logic*, (Dover ed.) New York 1959, pp. 66–70.

[2] H. S. Leonard 'Essences, Attributes and Predicates', *Proceedings and Addresses of the American Philosophical Association* **37** (1964) 25–51.

[3] So the conceptions of Kant's *Inaugural Dissertation* and Wittgenstein's *Tractatus* relate to the former; Sellars' 'extra-conceptual' possibilities to the latter.

[4] See MRM. At the Irvine Colloquium we followed the exposition of MRM, and Dana Scott pointed out the elegance gained by not trying to represent natural modality at the same time. However, in the course of a philosophical retrenchment such as is attempted in MRM, due attention should be given to the peculiarities of natural modality.

[5] Cf. R. Meyer and K. Lambert 'Universally Free Logic and Standard Quantification Theory' *The Journal of Symbolic Logic* **33** (1968) 8–26.

[6] Cf. the discussion in R. H. Thomason, 'Modal Logic and Metaphysics' in *The Logical Way of Doing Things* (ed. by K. Lambert), New Haven (1969).

[7] H. Putnam, 'Reds, Greens, and Logical Analysis', *Philosophical Review* **65** (1956) 206–217; A. Pap, 'Once More: Colors and the Synthetic A Priori', *Philosophical Review* **66** (1957), 94–99; H. Putnam, 'Rejoinder to Arthur Pap', *Philosophical Review* **66** (1957) 100–103.

[8] This was suggested by Professor T. Drange, West Virginia University, to Profs. R. Meyer, Bryn Mawr College, and K. Lambert, who subsequently constructed the counterexample which follows.

[9] S. A. Kripke, 'A Completeness Theorem in Modal Logic', *Journal of Symbolic Logic* **24** (1959), 1–14.

[10] See reference 7. This discussion concerns the kind of statements which provides the central examples in the debate about essentialism.

[11] For explicit consideration of such stronger description theories, see our 'On Free Description Theory', *Zeitschrift für math. Logik und Grundl. der Math.* **13** (1967) 225–240.

[12] See the paper cited in reference 11 and references therein.

[13] Note that $x = \mathbf{n}$ may be true when $\mathbf{n}$ is a name, in which case $\mathbf{n}$ is the name of a subsistent; if $E!x \& x = \mathbf{n}$ is true, $\mathbf{n}$ names an existent, and if $\Box x = \mathbf{n}$ is true then $\mathbf{n}$ is the name of a substance.

[14] See especially J. M. Dunn and N. D. Belnap, Jr. 'The Substitution Interpretation of the Quantifiers', *Nous* **2** (1968) 177–185, and H. Leblanc 'A simplified account of validity and implication for quantificational logic', *Journal of Symbolic Logic* **33** (1968) 231–235.

[15] H. Leonard, 'Essences, Attributes, and Predicates', *Proc. Amer. Philos. Assoc.* (1964).

[16] See Thomason, *op. cit.*, and 'Some Completeness Results for Modal Predicate Calculi' in the present volume, pp. 56–76. In this appendix we follow the more general exposition of MRM.

JAAKKO HINTIKKA

EXISTENTIAL PRESUPPOSITIONS AND UNIQUENESS PRESUPPOSITIONS

I. EXISTENTIAL PRESUPPOSITIONS

The meeting in the proceedings of which this paper appears was primarily devoted to presuppositionless logics, somewhat misleadingly known as free logics.[1] (The term misleads because of the absence of any connection between these 'free' logics and the well-known free algebras.) The presuppositions which these logics dispense with are presuppositions of existence, typically presuppositions to the effect that certain free singular terms are not empty.

I have some doubts as to how interesting an enterprise the study of such presuppositionless logics will turn out to be in the long run. It seems to me that a study of the role of existential presuppositions in first-order logic will fairly soon exhaust all the general theoretical interest that there is in the area, if conducted as a purely syntactical or semantical enterprise. It is true that there is a considerable variety of ways in which a semantics can be built for a presuppositionless first-order logic. However, a philosophically satisfactory comparison between them will in my opinion have to turn on a deeper conceptual analysis of the situation than the standard syntactical and semantical methods afford.

There are at least two main directions into which the study of presupposition-free logics can be developed so as to preserve its continued interest. One main direction which needs – and deserves – much more discussion than it has so far received is the deeper philosophical analysis of the concept of existence, on which the concept of existential presupposition is based. My original intention was to discuss a line of approach to this area which looks especially interesting. It seems to me that we have to go beyond the usual syntactical and semantical tools in order to get at the interesting problems here. What we study in semantics are roughly speaking a language plus the representative relations that connect it with its several interpretations.[2] What we do not study in semantics is what goes into these relations, that is, the dynamics of the interplay of language and reality when an applied language is actually being used to some purpose. Elsewhere,[3] I have suggested what the 'language-games' look like which go together with quantifiers – and therefore also with the concept of existence which is codified by the existential quantifier. I have argued that in this case the use of the frequently misapplied label 'language-game' need not give rise to any compunctions, for the games in question can be so called in the precise sense of the mathematical theory of games. I have even ventured to suggest that this game-theoretical interpretation of first-order logic can serve as a starting-point for interesting philosophical and logical theorizing. I have nevertheless decided not to take up here these in my judgment highly important matters, and decided to try to say instead something that seems to be more closely related to the other papers of this volume.

II. MODAL LOGICS AS 'FREE' LOGICS

A second main enterprise which seems very promising is to examine presuppositions of existence in languages richer than those studied in first-order logic. Among such richer languages, those using modal notions (including propositional attitudes) seem to be particularly interesting.

It seems to me that this is a most promising area for further work, although it also seems to me that most of the crucial insights required to see our way through have already been obtained. However, many of the consequences of these insights still remain in the dark. I surmise that future work in this area will have extremely important general philosophical implications. The problems to which this work seems relevant include such questions as e.g. the question as to what entities are needed in a satisfactory semantics for modal logics, the distinction between a theory of meaning and a theory of reference, and an evaluation of Quine's criticism of quantified modal logic.

Not all work in this direction may at first seem related to existential presuppositions. In this paper, I shall nevertheless argue that the presuppositions of uniqueness whose failure is responsible for the puzzling breakdown of some of the most characteristic laws of first-order logic (notably of the law of existential generalization) in modal contexts are to a surprising extent analogous to the presuppositions of existence which we need in first-order logic. Even the explicit formulation of these presuppositions in one's system of modal logic can be elicited in the same way as the famous 'Quinean' formulation '$(Ex)(x=b)$' of the existential presuppositions of first-order logic.[4] Hence almost any serious study of the semantics of modal logic will be related very closely to the study of logics without existential presuppositions. What one needs in the theory of modal logics is in my opinion quite literally a presuppositionless logic (or 'free logic', to use this unfortunate label), namely, a logic without presuppositions of uniqueness. To coin a slogan, modal logics are really only so many 'free' (i.e. presuppositionless) logics.

Since this point of fundamental importance to our general view of the whole field of presuppositionless logics and of its prospects, I shall try to argue for it, even on pain of occasionally repeating what I have said elsewhere.[5]

III. MODEL SETS AND MODEL SYSTEMS

I shall first discuss a quantified modal logic with '(Ex)', '(Ux)' as quantifiers and 'M', 'N' as the two (dual) modal operators. (I assume that they correspond, roughly, to necessity and possibility, but I shall leave their precise interpretations unspecified.) As propositional connectives, I shall employ '$\sim$', '&', '$\vee$', and I shall normally assume (for simplicity) that all negation-signs have been driven into the formulas so as to be prefixed to atomic ones or to identities.

I shall use the familiar framework of model sets and model systems. Dagfinn Føllesdal has criticized me repeatedly for speaking of them and not of the 'real' models and systems of models.[6] However, while I may have given the impression of overestimating the ease at which considerations pertaining to model sets can be transposed so as to apply to models, I think that he is still underestimating it. Later in the present paper, I shall say a few things about the relation of my methods to the usual semantical methods which hopefully illustrate this ease.

The conditions that define a model set (say μ) in first-order logic are well known, but still brief enough to be reproduced here:

(C.$\sim$) Not $p\in\mu$, $\sim p\in\mu$ (p atomic or an identity).
(C.&) If $(p \,\&\, q)\in\mu$, then $p\in\mu$, $q\in\mu$.
(C.$\vee$) If $(p \vee q)\in\mu$, then either $p\in\mu$ or $q\in\mu$ (or both).

(C.E) If $(Ex)p \in \mu$, then $p(a/x) \in \mu$ for at least one singular constant '*a*'.

(C.U) If $(Ux)p \in \mu$, and if '*b*' occurs in the formulas of μ, then $p(b/x) \in \mu$.

(C.self≠) Not '$(b \neq b)$' $\in \mu$.

(C.=) If p is atomic or an identity, if $p(a/b) = q(a/b)$, $p \in \mu$ and '$(a = b)$' $\in \mu$, then $q \in \mu$.

In (C.E), $p(a/x)$ is the result of substituting '*a*' for '*x*' everywhere in *p*. The same notation is used in (C.U) and (C.=), and will be used in what follows. In (C.self≠), '$(b \neq b)$' is of course a shorthand for '$\sim (b = b)$'.

A model system Ω is a set of model sets with a two-place relation (called the alternativeness relation) defined on it in such a way that the following conditions are satisfied:

(C.M*) If $Mp \in \mu \in \Omega$, there is an alternative $\lambda \in \Omega$ to μ such that $p \in \lambda$.

(C.N$^+$) If $Np \in \mu \in \Omega$ and if $\lambda \in \Omega$ is an alternative to μ, then $p \in \lambda$.

(C.refl) The alternativeness relation is reflexive.

Instead of (C.refl), we may want to adopt for some applications the weaker condition:

(C.n*) If $Np \in \mu \in \Omega$, there is at least one alternative $\lambda \in \Omega$ to μ such that $p \in \lambda$.

The satisfiability of a set of formulas λ is defined as its imbeddability in some member $\mu \supseteq \lambda$ of a model system Ω, $\mu \in \Omega$. When in the sequel I shall consider changes in the conditions defining a model system, I consider them substantial only when they affect the concept of satisfiability so defined.

A formula is said to be logically true if the unit set of its negation is not satisfiable.

Independently of what one thinks of the relation of my conditions to semantics proper, a certain plausibility cannot be denied of them, it seems to me. Model sets can obviously be thought of as (partial) descriptions of possible worlds, and alternatives to a member (say μ) of a model system can be thought of as descriptions of worlds 'alternative to' the one described by μ (in the case of necessity and possibility, of worlds that in some relevant sense could have been realized instead of the one described by μ). The basic intuitive idea is, roughly, that necessity (in a given possible world) equals truth in all alternative possible worlds, and that possibility therefore equals truth in at least one alternative possible world.

IV. THE BEHAVIOR OF IDENTITY IN MODAL CONTEXTS

(C.$\sim$) can be strengthened so as to omit the restriction to atomic formulas and identities. However, (C.$=$) cannot be so modified without affecting the concept of satisfiability and without creating paradoxical applications (when arbitrary free singular terms are substituted for our individual constants).

However, it can be shown that a weaker principle of substitutivity is a consequence of our conditions:

(C.N$=$) If $p \in \mu$, if p results from q by interchanging 'a' and 'b' in a number of places which are within the scope of precisely $n_2, n_2, \ldots$ modal operators, respectively, and if '$N^{n_1}(a=b)$' $\in \mu$, '$N^{n_2}(a=b)$' $\in \mu, \ldots$, then $q \in \mu$.

Here 'N^{n_1}' is of course a shorthand for '$NN \ldots N$' (n_1 occurrences of N), and similarly for the other n_i.

It can be shown that this holds independently of (C.refl). If this condition is assumed, then instead of the several iterated necessary identities we need only '$N^{n_0}(a=b)$' $\in \mu$ where $n_0 = \max(n_1, n_2, \ldots)$. The case $n_0 = 0$ is included in our formulation as a special case.

The semantic import of (C.N$=$) is clear. When a singular term occurs outside the scope of modal operators, we are speaking merely of its reference in the actual world. When one of its occurrences is buried under n_i layers of modal operators, we are speaking of its several references in the possible worlds described by all the different alternatives, n_i times removed, to the description of the actual one. In order for the terms 'a' and 'b' to be interchangeable at such an occurrence, they must refer to the same individual in each of these possible worlds. That this is the case is precisely what '$N^{n_i}(a=b)$' expresses. Thus (C.N$=$) is very plausible even without the possibility of reducing it to the simpler condition (C.$=$). No wonder, therefore, that occasionally it has been said that principles like (C.N$=$) are the form which the principle of the substitutivity of identity takes in modal contexts. It can be shown, however, that (C.N$=$)

follows from the other conditions (in the sense that it does not affect the notion of satisfiability), and hence does not embody any assumptions not already made in ordinary non-modal first-order logic.

A proof that the replacement of (C.=) by (C.N=) does not affect satisfiability is straightforward.[7]

If (C.=) is not restricted to atomic formulas and identities, various paradoxes will ensue. I shall not discuss them here, however, for the restriction already gives us a satisfactory (and intuitive) way of avoiding all the difficulties.

It might be thought that my giving up of the stronger (unrestricted) form of (C.=) leads to theoretical difficulties in connection with our concept of individual. (As Quine has insisted, Leibniz's law must hold for individuals – otherwise there is something wrong with the very notion.) However, I shall suggest later in this paper that the justified and true element in Quine's claim can be caught in a different way without modifying at all what has been said so far.

V. A PARADOX INDEPENDENT OF IDENTITY

It is readily seen that some changes are needed in (C.E) and (C.U) to avoid paradoxical applications similar to those that arise in connection with the strong form of (C.=). The following implication is a case in point:

(1) $N(a=a) \supset (Ex)N(x=a)$.

Reading 'a' = 'the next president of the United States', the antecedent of (1) says that necessarily the next president is the next president, which is obviously true. The consequent says that there is someone who necessarily is the next president, i.e. whose election is inevitable. On any reasonable interpretation of necessity, this is false. Hence (1) is (contingently) false.

Yet it would be logically true if our definitions were accepted unmodified. This may be seen as follows: Assume that (1) is not logically true, i.e. assume that there is a model system Ω and a model set $\mu \in \Omega$ such that

(2) '$N(a=a)$'$\in \mu \in \Omega$ counter-assumption
(3) '$(Ux)M(x \neq a)$'$\in \mu \in \Omega$ counter-assumption.

Then it follows:

(4) $`M(a \neq a)' \in \mu$ from (3) by (C.U).

Here (4) and (2) violate the stronger form of (C.$\sim$), showing the impossibility of (2)–(3) and hence the logical truth of (1). If the stronger form is not available, we can argue as follows:

(5) $`(a \neq a)' \in \lambda$ for some alternative $\lambda \in \Omega$ to μ, by (C.M*).

Here (5) violates (C.self $\neq$), yielding the same conclusion.

Extremely simple though this argument is, it deserves several comments. Its very simplicity shows – or at least very strongly suggests – that the only possible source of trouble here is the condition (C.U). The other conditions relied on were (C.$\sim$) (or alternatively (C.self $\neq$)) and (C.M*), none of which is subject to reasonable doubts in this context. (Furthermore, denying the possibility of our preliminary simplifications presupposes giving up classical logic in a fairly radical way.) Moreover, contrary to many suggestions, the trouble cannot be blamed on the failure of the substitutivity of identity in modal contects, for (C.=) was not used in the argument at all. Nor can the paradoxical result be laid to the possibility of illicitly 'importing' new individuals to model sets – a phenomenon known to cause trouble elsewhere.[8]

Our example is similar to Quine's favorite brand of illustrations. Instead of 'proving' (1), we likewise could have 'proved'

'N(the number of planets = the number of planets) $\supset$
$(Ex)N$(the number of planets = x)'.

The fact that the fallaciousness of our proof does not turn at all on our assumptions concerning identity belies (it seems to me) Quine's (and Føllesdal's) emphasis on the failure of the substitutivity of identity as the source of trouble in this area.[9]

Doubts are perhaps raised concerning my claim that (1) is false. It seems to me obvious, however, that on the intended interpretation of (1) it *is* false, and that these doubts can be traced to what we are inclined to say of the translation of (1) into more or less ordinary discourse and of the logical behavior of this translation. What is being presupposed by the above conditions is clearly an interpretation of '*M*' such that *Mp* is true in a possible world iff *p* were true in at least one alternative possible world. If we understand the notion of alternativeness, we can understand this independently of how we are inclined to express ourselves in ordinary language. Here, we do not even need more than a rudimentary understanding of what is involved, for all that is presupposed by the truth of the antecedent of (1) is that there is no possible world in which it is true to assert '$a \neq a$'. And this much is surely completely uncontroversial.

The same line of thought suggests that we cannot very well doubt the applicability of (C.self$\neq$) on the intended interpretation.

I am not saying that it is impossible to try to interpret modal operators in some other way, at least *ad hoc*. However, no interpretation essentially different from mine has ever been given a satisfactory semantic development. The onus is thus on those who want to understand the antecedent of (1) in some way different from mine. Moreover, even if an alternative interpretation of (1) (or perhaps rather of its translation into an 'ordinary language') can be given, I am sure it will turn out to be analyzable in terms of the interpretation I am presupposing. (Later, I shall in fact indicate one such interpretation of the antecedent of an ordinary-language statement reminiscent of (1).) And even if there are irreducible competing readings, I can have my paradox (counter-example to the above conditions) simply by restricting my attention to the intended reading of (1).

In case you are here worried about the possible failure of *a* to exist, you are welcome to replace (1) by

(1*) '$((Ex)(x=a)\ \&\ N(a=a)) \supset (Ex)N(x=a)$'

which is as paradoxical as (1) and which can be shown to be logically true in the same way as (1) even when existential presuppositions are eliminated. The only additional assumption we have to make here is that there is such a person as the next president of the United States, i.e., that the United States will continue as a democracy – a factual assumption which I hope we are entitled to make.

Hence the truth of the antecedent of (1) on the intended interpretation is beyond doubt. The same is the case with the falsity of the consequent, again given the intended interpretation. In this case, the relevant aspect of the interpretation is the idea that bound (bindable) variables take ordinary individuals (e.g. persons) as their values. I hope that I do not have to try to justify this assumption here after everything Quine and Føllesdal have said concerning its indispensability.

Instead of rehearsing their weighty and eloquent reasons I shall merely register the fact that this assumption amply justifies my claim that the consequent of (1) is false. For who among the actual candidates is the invincible one? The labors of the supporters of the several candidates suggest that they at least are not convinced of the historical (and even less of the logical) necessity of their favorite's being nominated and elected.

The underlying semantical reason why the existential generalization (1) (or (1*) fails is also obvious. Under the different courses of events that are in fact possible the term 'the next president of the U.S.' refers to different politicians. Hence we cannot go from a statement, however true, about these different individuals to a statement which says that there is some one (unique) individual of which the same is true.

VI. AN AMBIGUITY IN ORDINARY LANGUAGE

Moreover, in addition to justifying the falsity of the consequent, Quine's assumption perhaps also helps to remove a residual awkwardness about the truth of the antecedent of (1). I am not denying that such ordinary-language statements as

(6) 'the next president of the United States is necessarily the next president of the United States'

can occasionally be understood so as to be false.

In general, my basic semantical idea of 'possible worlds' shows that almost any ordinary-language statement in which a singular term occurs within a modal context is in principle potentially ambiguous. Such a statement can sometimes be understood in (at least) two different ways. It can be taken to be about the different individuals which the term picks out in the different possible worlds that the modal operator invites us to consider. However, often it can also be understood as being about the unique individual to which the term in fact refers (i.e. refers in the actual world). More specifically, one faces this choice of interpretations at each occurrence of the term. For instance, the two interpretations of the first occurrence of 'the next president of the U.S.' in (6) yield

(7) 'necessarily whoever is the next president of the U.S. is identical with whoever is the next president of the U.S.'

and

(8) 'the man who in fact will be the next president of the U.S. is necessarily identical with the next president of the U.S.',

respectively. The former (7) is what we took '$N(a=a)$' to express. Because bound variables range over actual individuals, the latter (8) can be formalized by

(8*) '$(Ex)\,(x=a\ \&\ N(x=a))$'

or perhaps rather by

(8**) '$(x)\,(x=a \supset N(x=a))$'.

Unlike (7), (8)–(8**) can certainly be false – and in fact seem to be so. If you felt uncomfortable about my bland initial assertion that the antecedent of (1) is true, you had some right to do so, for the best translation of the antecedent into ordinary language admits of an interpretation which makes it false. This does not belie my point, however, that under the intended interpretation (1) is in fact false. On the contrary, our observations dispose of a plausible (but false) reason for doubting my suggestion.

VII. MODIFYING THE QUANTIFIER CONDITIONS

The main thing we have established by all of this is that the condition (C.U) has to be modified. But how? It is here that my principal working hypothesis comes in. The only essential assumption I shall make is that somehow or other we can modify (or amplify, if need be) our language so that the desired condition on which (C.U) can be restored can be expressed in the language itself.

This is not quite enough, however, for we must be able to allow for slightly different conditions depending on how 'x' occurs in p. Here our semantical point of view yields useful hints. Obviously, whatever goes wrong with (1) is due to the fact that under different courses of events we consider possible 'a' refers to different individuals. To forestall this, it must be required as an additional premise that 'a' does not exhibit this kind of referential multiplicity. Likewise, a further clause is needed in the requirements (C.U) which was used in the 'proof' of (1). What this additional condition must express is here the uniqueness of the reference of '*b*' in all the different possible worlds as a member of which we are considering '*x*' in *p*.

This is determined by the number of modal operators within the scope of which the variable '*x*' occurs at its different appearances in *p*. Let us assume that these numbers are $n_1, n_2, \ldots$. This fact will in the sequel be expressed by saying that the *modal profile* of *p* with respect to '*x*' is $n_1, n_2 \ldots$. Let us assume that in these circumstances some (so far completely unspecified) formula

(9) '$Q^{n_1, n_2, \ldots}(b)$'

expresses the desired condition. The only thing we are assuming about (9) is that the only free singular term in it is *b*. Then it is obvious how the crucial condition (C.U) has to be reformulated:

($C.U_q$) If $(Ux)p \in \mu \in \Omega$, if the modal profile of *p* with respect to '*x*' is $n_1, n_2, \ldots$ and if '*b*' occurs in the formulas of some member of Ω, then $[p(b/x) \vee \sim Q^{n_1, n_2, \ldots}(b)] \in \mu$.[10]

Here '*b*' is to all intents and purposes a completely arbitrary free singular term. The requirement that it appears in the members of some $\lambda \in \Omega$ is inserted simply to avoid having to speak of an unlimited class of free singular terms.

It is also clear that we have to change the dual condition (C.E) likewise. From the truth of an existentially quantified statement, more follows than the truth of some substitution-instance. A substitution-instance with respect to a term with the right sort of unique reference can always be introduced *salva* consistency:

($C.E_q$) If $(Ex)p \in \mu$, and if the modal profile of *p* with respect to '*x*' is $n_1, n_2, \ldots$ then $p(a/x) \in \mu$ and '$Q^{n_1, n_2, \ldots}(a)$' $\in \mu$ for some '*a*'.

VIII. THE MODIFICATION OF QUANTIFIER CONDITIONS IS UNIQUELY DETERMINED

The remarkable thing is that ($C.E_q$)–($C.U_q$) suffice, together with the rest of our conditions and conventions, to determine what the logical power of '$Q^{n_1, n_2, \dots}(b)$' is in the sense of showing how it can be expressed in our original symbolism. Given one further assumption we can show that the following formula is logically true:[11]

(10) '$(Ex)\,[N^{n_1}(x = b)\ \&\ N^{n_2}(x = b)\ \&\ \cdots] \equiv Q^{n_1, n_2, \dots}(b)$'.

In order to prove this, it suffices to prove implications in both directions. In order to prove such an implication, it suffices to reduce *ad absurdum* the assumption that its antecedent and the denial of its consequent are satisfiable together, i.e., can occur in the same member μ of a modal system Ω. This can be done as follows:

Left to right: Assume (counter-assumption)

(11) '$(Ex)\,[N^{n_1}(x = b)\ \&\ N^{n_2}(x = b)\ \&\cdots]$' $\in \mu \in \Omega$

and

(12) '$\sim Q^{n_1, n_2, \dots}(b)$' $\in \mu$.

Then by ($C.E_q$) we have for some '*a*'

(13) '$[N^{n_1}(a = b)\ \&\ N^{n_2}(a = b)\ \&\cdots]$' $\in \mu$

(14) '$Q^{n_1, n_2, \dots}(a)$' $\in \mu$.

Furthermore, we have from (13) by (C.&)

(15) '$N^{n_1}(a = b)$' $\in \mu$

'$N^{n_2}(a = b)$' $\in \mu$

Now at this stage we have to make some assumptions in order to get anywhere. We have to assume that with respect to the substitutivity of identity '$Q^{n_1, n_2, \dots}(b)$' behaves in the same way as a formula whose modal profile with respect to '*b*' is $n_1, n_2, \dots$ It is very hard to see how this could fail to be the case, for '$Q^{n_1, n_2, \dots}(b)$' is intended to guarantee the uniqueness of reference of the term '*b*' precisely in the same possible worlds as a member of which a sentence *p* speaks of *b* when the modal profile of *p* with respect to '*b*' is $n_1, n_2, \dots$ In short, as far as *b* is concerned, '$Q^{n_1, n_2, \dots}(b)$' speaks of the same possible worlds as *p* and might therefore be expected to behave vis-à-vis substitution in the same way as a sentence with the same profile as *p*. What this assumption means is that (C.N=) is applicable to (14) and (15), yielding

(16) '$Q^{n_1, n_2, \dots}(b)$' $\in \mu$.

Assuming the stronger form of (C.$\sim$), this contradicts (12) and therefore proves the desired implication.

Right to left: Assume (by way of counter-example) that

(17) $\text{`}Q^{n_1, n_2, \cdots}(b)\text{'} \in \mu \in \Omega$

and that

(18) $\text{`}(Ux)\,[M^{n_1}(x \neq b) \vee M^{n_2}(x \neq b) \vee \cdots]\text{'} \in \mu.$

Then we have from (17)–(18) by (C.U$_q$)

(19) $\text{`}\sim Q^{n_1, n_2, \cdots}(b) \vee [M^{n_1}(b \neq b) \vee M^{n_2}(b \neq b) \vee \cdots]\text{'} \in \mu$

Hence by (C.$\vee$) we have either $\text{`}\sim Q^{n_1, n_2, \cdots}(b)\text{'} \in \mu$ which is excluded by (17) and the stronger form of (C.$\sim$), or else

(20) $\text{`}M^{n_i}(b \neq b)\text{'} \in \mu$

for some i. From (20) we have by n_i applications of (C.M*)

(21) $\text{`}(b \neq b)\text{'} \in \lambda$

for some alternative λ to μ (n_i times removed from μ). But (21) violates (C.self $\neq$), showing the impossibility of (17)–(18), thus proving the desired implication, and thereby demonstrating the logical truth of (10).

Thus there is no need to introduce any new symbolism. The auxiliary condition that guarantees uniqueness can be expressed in our original notation. Nor is there any choice as to what the interrelation of the auxiliary condition to other formulas is. In fact, we can simply replace (C.U$_q$) and (C.E$_q$) by the following conditions:[12]

(C.U$_1$) If $(Ux)p \in \mu \in \Omega$, if the modal profile of p with respect to 'x' is $n_1, n_2, \ldots$, and if 'b' occurs in the formulas of some member of Ω, then $\text{`}\sim (Ex)(N^{n_1}(x=b) \,\&\, N^{n_2}(x=b) \,\&\, \cdots) \vee p(b/x)\text{'} \in \mu$.

(C.E$_1$) If $(Ex)p \in \mu$, and if the modal profile of p with respect to 'x' is $n_1, n_2, \ldots$, then, for some 'a', $p(a/x) \in \mu$ and $\text{`}(Ex)\,(N^{n_1}(x=a) \,\&\, N^{n_2}(x=a) \,\&\, \ldots)\text{'} \in \mu$.

It is understood that the order of conjuncts does not matter here. Moreover, we can require in (C.E$_1$) also that every formula obtained from

(*) $\text{`}(Ex\;\; (N^{n_1}(x=a) \,\&\, N^{n_2}(x=a) \,\&\, \cdots]\text{'}$

by omitting some of the conjuncts is also in μ. In fact, we shall require in general that these shorter formulas are in μ if (*) is in it.

We have seen that, given the assumptions indicated above, the conditions ($C.U_1$) and ($C.E_1$) are essentially the only way of reconciling quantification into modal contexts with the usual semantical conditions for logical constants. The solution which they present to the problem of quantifying into modal contexts can also be motivated directly in intuitive terms. Quine's criticism of quantified modal logic is predicated on the idea that quantifiers range over genuine, well-defined individuals. Now a free singular term (say '*a*') which picks out different individuals in the different possible worlds one is considering cannot specify such a well-defined individual. In order for '*a*' to specify a unique individual, there must be some *one and the same* individual to which it refers in all the possible worlds one must take into account. But this is just what (*) expresses in the case in which the relevant possible worlds are those n_1, n_2,... steps removed from the one μ describes. Hence what ($C.U_1$) and ($C.E_1$) imply may be partially expressed by saying that according to them a singular term is an acceptable substitution-value for a bound variable if and only if it picks out one and the same individual in all the relevant possible worlds. These possible worlds are of course precisely the ones as members of which one considered the values of the bound variable '*x*' in the quantified sentences $(Ex)\,p$ and $(Ux)\,p$ mentioned in ($C.U_1$) and ($C.E_1$). These conditions thus say just what one can expect on the basis of the Quinean interpretation of quantification in the first place.[13]

It is especially important to appreciate this semantical situation in view of the widespread misinterpretations of the intended role of our uniqueness premises (22) or (24). Their function has frequently been taken to be to restrict somehow the range of individuals over which one's bound variables range. This is a serious (and, it seems to me, unprovoked) oversimplification. (This misinterpretation has been perpetrated, among others, by Hector-Neri Castañeda and Wilfrid Sellars.) When we have to consider our individuals as members of several possible worlds, the whole notion of 'ranging over' becomes so oversimplified as to be of little explanatory value, and we cannot in any case describe satisfactorily the role of the uniqueness premises in terms of this notion. A restriction on the range of one's bound variables restricts them to some subset of actually existing individuals. What our quantifier conditions ($C.E_1$) and

($C.U_1$) involve is not this sort of restricted quantification, but a recognition of the fact that we have to consider those individuals over which bound variables 'range' as members of several possible worlds. This necessitates spelling out the fact that in considering one particular 'value' of a bound variable we must consider *one and the same* individual in all the relevant possible worlds. This is what ($C.E_1$) and ($C.U_1$) accomplish, and it is completely obvious that this task cannot be performed by ordinary relativization of quantifiers ranging over actual objects.

IX. GENERALIZATIONS

These considerations can be extended to the case in which we have any number of pairs of modal operators '$N^{(i)}$', '$M^{(i)}$'. We shall assume that they are distinguished from each other by superscripts. Furthermore, these operators may be relativized to an individual or a set of individuals, to be indicated by a subscript. (It is convenient to assume that one of the available subscripts stands for a 'null individual' which characterizes an unrelativized modality). Semantically speaking, each new subscript brings in a new alternativeness relation. (These different relations may of course be interrelated in different ways.) For the time being we assume that no bound variables occur as subscripts to modal operators.

The occurrence of free singular terms as subscripts of modal operators necessitates a dual extension of (C.=) to cover this case:

(C.=N) If '$(a=b)$'$\in\mu$ and $N_a p\in\mu$, then $N_b p\in\mu$.
(C.=M) If '$(a=b)$'$\in\mu$ and if $M_a p\in\mu$, then $M_b p\in\mu$.

Here 'N', 'M' are assumed to be any modal operators to which subscripts can be attached.

Let us now consider an occurrence of 'x' in p. If the modal operators (in order) within the scope of which 'x' occurs at this place are characterized by the subscripts and superscripts $^{(i_1)}_{a_1}, ^{(i_2)}_{a_2}, \ldots$, then this list is said to indicate the *modal character* of the occurrence in question. (Notice that the subscript of an operator is thought of as being *outside* the scope of that operator.) A sequence of the modal characters of all the occurrences of 'x' in p will be called (by modifying our earlier definition somewhat) the *modal profile* of p with respect to 'x'.

It is easy to see how the above conditions ($C.U_1$) and ($C.E_1$) are to be modified so as to apply to this general case. The only change needed concerns the auxiliary formula that takes over the role of

$$(22) \qquad (Ex)\,(N^{n_1}(x=b)\ \&\ N^{n_2}(x=b)\ \&\cdots).$$

If the modal profile of p with respect to 'x' is

$$(23) \qquad \overset{(i_{11})}{a_{11}}\ \overset{(i_{12})}{a_{12}}\ldots,\ \overset{(i_{21})}{a_{21}}\ \overset{(i_{22})}{a_{22}}\ldots,\ \ldots$$

then the role of (22) will be played by the formula

$$(24) \qquad \text{'}(Ex)\,[N^{(i_{11})}_{a_{11}}\,N^{(i_{12})}_{a_{12}}\cdots(x=b)\ \&\ N^{(i_{21})}_{a_{21}}\,N^{(i_{22})}_{a_{22}}\cdots(x=b)\ \&\cdots]\text{'}.$$

Otherwise, the resulting conditions $(C.U_m)$ and $(C.E_m)$ will be like $(C.U_1)$ and $(C.E_1)$.

If the alternativeness relation that goes together with a pair of modal operators – say '$N^{(i)}$', '$M^{(i)}$' – is transitive, then in (24) repetitions of '$N^{(i)}$' (with the same subscript, if any) can be disregarded. Interrelations between different modal operators (or with the same modal operator with different subscripts) have to be studied *in casu*.

Apart from this qualification, our formulations above seem to cover almost everything that is needed for a satisfactory treatment of modal logics, including modal logics with several different kinds of modal operators.

X. EXISTENTIAL PRESUPPOSITIONS AS SPECIAL CASES OF UNIQUENESS PRESUPPOSITIONS

Several comments are in order here which may elucidate further the import of what I have said.

In the formulations $(C.U_1)$ and $(C.E_1)$, the case $n_i=0$ was included. Then N^{n_i} will be an empty sequence of N's, and (22) will contain a conjunct of the form '$(x=b)$'. The corresponding possibility that the modal character of some of the occurrences of 'x' in p in the empty sequence is likewise assumed to be needed, yielding a conjunct of the form '$(x=b)$' in (24). In case no modal operators are around at all, these are all the cases we have to worry about. Then the crucial clauses (22) and (24) which serve to guard us against failures of uniqueness reduce to clauses of the form '$(Ex)\,(x=b)$' which express the familiar existential presuppositions. The necessity of formulating the presuppositions precisely in this way emerges as a special case of the argument given above. This brings out what I meant in the beginning of this paper when I emphasized that what we need in modal logic is an elimination of uniqueness presuppositions analogous to the elimination of existential presuppositions. The failure of our usual logical laws in modal contexts, signalled by the invalidity of (1), can be traced to the fact that not all our singular terms will exhibit the right kind of uniqueness of reference when different possible worlds are compared with each other. Hence in our basic conditions for existence and universality we cannot assume such uniqueness, which has to be postulated explicitly when it holds. We have seen that these uniqueness presuppositions and existence presuppositions can both be uncovered by one and the same argument.

XI. FURTHER OBSERVATIONS. THE PARITY OF IDENTICAL INDIVIDUALS

Among other things, we can now also see what went wrong in our 'proof' of (1). In order to get (4) from (2)–(3), we would need an additional assumption

(25) $\text{`}(Ex)N(x = a)\text{'} \in \mu$

which not only is false but which would contradict (3) in virtue of (C.$\sim$). The 'proof' of (1) is thus strictly a *petitio principii.*

These observations give us a considerable chunk of modal logic in a semi-semantical formulation. It is easily seen, among other things, that none of the famous critical formulas will be logically true whose truth depends on 'moving individuals from one possible world to another', i.e. depends on assuming that whenever an individual exists in one world, it exists in certain others.[14] It is easy to construct a counter-example e.g. to the Barcan formula and to formulas of the form

(26) $(Ex)Np \supset N(Ex)p$

where we may for simplicity assume that p is atomic.[15] Hence the annoying necessity of having to modify (C.N^{+}) and perhaps even *modus ponens* is automatically avoided.[16]

There is a further point, however, that deserves to be made. We have discovered that whenever (in the presence of a single pair of modal operators) the modal profile of p with respect to 'x' is $n_1, n_2, \ldots$, then

(27) $\text{'}(Ex)\,(N^{n_1}(x = b)\ \&\ N^{n_2}(x = b)\ \&\ \ldots)\text{'}$

suffices to restore existential generalization with respect to 'b' in $p(b/x)$ so as to yield $(Ex)p$. In fact, the force of (27) could almost be expressed by reading it 'b is an individual' (i.e. for the purposes of a context with the same modal profile as p). But if this restoration of the reference of 'b' to the status of a 'real' individual is to succeed, it might be suggested, then the same auxiliary premises should restore the substitutivity of identity, too. For the same things should really be said of identical individuals. This suggests adopting the following condition:

(C.ind=) If $p \in \mu$, '$(a=b)$'$\in \mu$, and if q results from p by interchanging 'a' and 'b' in a number of places which are within the scope of $n_1, n_2, \ldots$ modal operators, respectively, and if

$$\text{'}(Ex)\,[(x = a)\ \&\ N^{n_1}(x = a)\ \&\ N^{n_2}(x = a)\ \&\cdots]\text{'} \in \mu$$
$$\text{'}(Ex)\,[(x = b)\ \&\ N^{n_1}(x = b)\ \&\ N^{n_2}(x = b)\ \&\cdots]\text{'} \in \mu$$

then $q \in \mu$.

Here the displayed existentially quantified formulas may be replaced by some of their admissible variants, i.e. by formulas obtained from them by trading 'x' for some other bound variable and/or changing the order of some identities and conjunctions. In view of (C.N=), (C.ind=) is equivalent to the following condition:

(C.ind$=_0$) If '$(a=b)$'$\in \mu$,

$$\text{'}(Ex)\,[(x = a)\ \&\ N^{n_1}(x = a)\ \&\ N^{n_2}(x = a)\ \&\cdots]\text{'} \in \mu,$$
$$\text{'}(Ex)\,[(x = b)\ \&\ N^{n_1}(x = b)\ \&\ N^{n_2}(x = b)\ \&\cdots]\text{'} \in \mu,$$

then $\text{'}[N^{n_1}(a = b)\ \&\ N^{n_2}(a = b)\ \&\cdots]\text{'} \in \mu$.

(Here the existentially quantified formulas may again be replaced by suitable admissible variants of theirs.)

The reason why the first conjuncts '$(x=a)$' and '$(x=b)$' are needed in (C.ind=) and (C.ind$=_0$) is obvious. In order for the 'actual' identity '$(a=b)$' to have any effects, the references of 'a' and 'b' have to be 'genuine individuals' also in so far as the world described by μ is concerned.

Apparently for many modalities (C.ind=) is an acceptable condition.

(There are rather plausible-looking counter-examples to it in epistemic logic. I believe that I can nevertheless explain them away. To attempt to do it here would take us too far, however.[17]) The way in which it can be generalized so as to apply when several pairs of modal operators (with or without subscripts) are present should be obvious on the basis of our earlier discussion.

XII. QUINE VINDICATED (?)

It seems to me that (C.ind=) really brings out the true element in Quine's emphasis on the substitutivity of identity as a test of the normality of our interpretation of the concept of individual. The true element, I submit, is the parity of identical *individuals*. Not any two singular terms which pick out the same individual in the actual world are intersubstitutable in modal contexts, for they may refer to different individuals in other possible worlds we have to consider. However, whatever is said of a genuine (unique) *individual* can always be said of another individual identical with it. This is precisely what (C.ind=) spells out when the notion of an individual is relativized to a particular context (class of possible worlds).[18]

By the same token, 'genuine individuals' in the sense just indicated must exhibit other kinds of nice predictable behavior. One fairly obvious requirement of this sort is the following:

(C.ind=E) If '$(a=b)$'$\in\mu$

'$(Ex)\,[(x=a)\ \&\ N^{n_1}(x=a)\ \&\ N^{n_2}(x=a)\ \&\cdots]$'$\in\mu$

'$(Ex)\,[(x=b)\ \&\ N^{m_1}(x=b)\ \&\ N^{m_2}(x=b)\ \&\cdots]$'$\in\mu$

then

'$(Ex)\,[(x=a)\ \&\ (x=b)\ \&\ N^{n_1}(x=x)\ \&\ N^{n_2}(x=x)\ \&\cdots\ \&$
$N^{m_1}(x=x)\ \&\ N^{m_2}(x=x)\ \&\cdots]$'$\in\mu$.

Instead of the first two existentially quantified formulas, we may here have any admissible variants of theirs.

The intuitive motivation of (C.ind=E) will be commented on later. Meanwhile, it may be pointed out that together (C.ind=) and (C.ind=E) seem to catch Quine's intentions very well. By their means the validity of all formulas of the following form can be demonstrated:

(28) $(Ux)\,(Uy)\,((x=y)\supset(p\supset q))$

where p and q are like each other except for an interchange of 'x' and 'y' at a number of places. Now it is in terms of these formulas that Quine frequently formulates his point about the substitutivity of identity. Moreover, the reasons Quine actually gives for the substitutivity principle are admirably suited to motivate the adoption of a principle of parity for identical *individuals*, whereas I do not see that they carry any weight whatsoever as a defense of the substitutivity of *de facto* coreferential free singular terms, i.e. as a defense of the unqualified form of (C.=). One general defect of Quine's and Føllesdal's discussions of the substitutivity principle seems to be a failure to emphasize sufficiently the distinction between the different variants of the principle.

In order to see that the bound-variable version of the substitutivity principle (28) is valid, we may argue as follows:

(29) $(Ex)(Ey)((x = y) \,\&\, p \,\&\, \sim q) \in \mu \in \Omega.$

This is the counter-assumption (for some model set μ and modal system Ω). It can be reduced *ad absurdum* as follows:

(30) $(Ey)((a = y) \,\&\, p(a/x) \,\&\, \sim q(a/x)) \in \mu$

(31) '$(Ex)[(x = a) \,\&\, N^{n_1}(x = a) \,\&\, N^{n_2}(x = a) \,\&\, \cdots]$' $\in \mu$

(32) $(a = b) \,\&\, p(a/x)(b/y) \,\&\, \sim q(a/x)(b/y) \in \mu$

(33) '$(Ex)[(x = b) \,\&\, N^{m_1}(x = b) \,\&\, N^{m_2}(x = b) \,\&\, \cdots]$' $\in \mu$.

Here $n_1, n_2, \ldots$ is the modal profile of p with respect to 'x' and $m_1, m_2, \ldots$ the modal profile of q with respect to 'y'. Of these steps, (30)–(31) follow from (29) by (C.E$_1$), and (32)–(33) follow from (30) likewise.

From (32) we have by (C.&)

(34) '$(a = b)$' $\in \mu$

(35) $p(a/x)(b/y) \in \mu$

(36) $\sim q(a/x)(b/y) \in \mu$.

From (31), (33) and (34) we obtain by (C.ind=E)

(37) '$(Ex)[(x = a) \,\&\, (x = b) \,\&\, N^{n_1}(x = x) \,\&\, N^{n_2}(x = x) \,\&\, \cdots \,\&\, N^{m_1}(x = x) \,\&\, N^{m_2}(x = x) \,\&\, \cdots]$' $\in \mu$.

Hence we have by (C.E$_1$) and (C.&) for some 'd'

(38) '$(d = a)$' $\in \mu$

(39) '$(d = b)$' $\in \mu$

(40) '$(Ex)\,[(x = d)\ \&\ N^{n_1}(x = d)\ \&\ N^{n_2}(x = d)\ \&\cdots\&$
$N^{m_1}(x = d)\ \&\ N^{m_2}(x = d)\ \&\cdots]$' $\in \mu$

and therefore *a fortiori*

(41) '$(Ex)\,[(x = d)\ \&\ N^{n_1}(x = d)\ \&\ N^{n_2}(x = d)\ \&\cdots]$' $\in \mu$

(42) '$(Ex)\,[(x = d)\ \&\ N^{m_2}(x = d)\ \&\ N^{m_2}(x = d)\ \&\cdots]$' $\in \mu$.

By (C.ind=) we now have from (35), (31), and (41)

(43) $p(d/x)(b/y) \in \mu$

and in the same way from (43), (33), and (42)

(44) $p(d/x)(d/y) \in \mu$.

By the same line of argument but starting from (36) instead of (35) we have

(45) $\sim q(d/x)(d/y) \in \mu$.

But $p(d/x)(d/y)$ and $q(d/x)(d/y)$ are by assumption identical. Hence (44) and (45) violate the stronger form of (C.$\sim$). This contradiction completes our reductive argument and hence establishes the desired validity.

It is seen at the same time, however, that Quine's emphasis on the substitutivity of identity as the main test that our concept of an individual is all right may not have been entirely happy, even when his point is interpreted in the way we just did. Quine is absolutely right in insisting that the only way of carrying out the normal, intended interpretation of quantification is to require that bound variables range over genuine individuals. What this leads us to, however, is primarily a modification of our conditions on quantifiers, and only secondarily an addition to our conditions on identities. (In fact, we have seen that at least some of the paradoxes that otherwise ensue arise independently of our ways with identity.) The conditions (C.ind=) and (C.ind=E) which serve to satisfy Quine's requirement concerning the substitutivity of identity embody happy afterthoughts rather than indispensable elements of our treatment of identity.

What we have found contains the essential features of a general theory of modality – both for the case of a single pair of modal operators and for the general case of any number of pairs of operators. What is missing is (*inter alia*) a treatment of the case in which bound variables occur as subscripts. No such treatment will be attempted here. A discerning reader may perhaps already perceive what form it can take when conducted e.g. in terms of the ε-technique of Hilbert.

Another topic that will largely be left untouched here is the question of the special assumptions which can be made concerning different particular modalities (e.g. various assumptions concerning the properties of their alternativeness relations, such as transitivity, reflexivity absolutely or under certain conditions, symmetry, etc.) They will have to be dealt with in various special theories of particular modal notions, it seems to me.

XIII. EPISTEMIC LOGIC

Among other things, we obtain in this way a formulation of epistemic logic which is in some respects a modified and extended version of the system presented in my book *Knowledge and Belief.*

The main additional assumption we may want to make here is (I have argued) the transitivity of the epistemic alternativeness relation. Or, rather, this assumption characterizes philosophers' strong sense of knowledge in which it is contrasted to merely possessing true information. In the presence of just one pair of epistemic notions K_a, P_a (corresponding to 'N' and 'M', and expressing what the bearer of 'a' knows and his 'epistemic possibility', respectively) the only possible types of auxiliary premises (uniqueness and/or existence presuppositions) will then be of the following kinds

(46) '$(Ex)\,(x = b \;\&\; K_a(x = b))$'

(47) '$(Ex)\,K_a(x = b)$'

(48) '$(Ex)\,(x = b)$'

depending on whether we are considering a formula in which 'b' occurs both inside and outside the scopes of 'K_a' and/or 'P_a', only inside, or only outside.

It is important to realize that these three conditions are – or at least can be assumed to be – logically independent apart from the fact that (46) logically implies the other two. (This implication follows easily from the assumptions made earlier.) The independence shows that, although existence presuppositions and uniqueness presuppositions are largely parallel to each other and although they can be discussed essentially in the same way, they are nevertheless materially different assumptions. The cases in which the implication from (47) to (48) fails are likely to be somewhat marginal, but I do not see any persuasive reasons why they should be ruled out. They will amount to cases where *a* knows who (or what) someone (or something is, 'should he (or it) exist', although it so happens that he (it) does not. Allowing for such cases seems a natural course in view of certain puzzling examples, though it does not seem to be an indispensable way out of these difficulties.

Likewise, disallowing the implication from (47) and (48) together to (46) would not lead to a violation of any other assumptions we are likely to make concerning the notion of knowledge. However, the 'success grammar' of knowing makes this implication a very natural assumption.

The independence of the analogues to (46)–(48) is of course completely obvious in the case of belief instead of knowledge.

Part of the force of the transitivity assumptions which characterizes the strong sense of knowledge can be caught by the following 'transfer assumption':

(C.EK=EK=*) If '$(Ex)\, K_a(x=b)$'$\in\mu\in\Omega$ and if $\lambda\in\Omega$ is an epistemic alternative to μ with respect to '*a*', then '$(Ex)\, K_a(x=b)$'$\in\lambda$.

XIV. MODELS FOR MODEL SYSTEMS

So far I have not said anything about the kind of 'real' semantics that might go together with my semi-semantical treatment. I suspect that in the study of modal notions, a treatment of their logic by reference to model sets and model systems is in fact simpler and more straightforward than a treatment in ordinary semantical terms. Nevertheless, a few words about what a genuine semantics for my modal logics will look like might clarify the situation and also clarify the relation of my approach to that used by other logicians.[19]

My treatment involves, first of all, an innocuous assumption that we have a name available for each individual and for each entity of any other type that we want to consider. I shall not pause to rehearse the standard objections to this simplifying assumption or the equally standard rejoinders that can be made to these objections. A similar procedure is in any case familiar enough in ordinary non-modal logic.

The main effect of this simplifying assumption is that we can in most cases formulate the truth-conditions of sentences of different kinds very easily in terms of truth-conditions for certain simpler sentences. This is essentially what happens in the conditions defining a model set and a model system. The reason why we need a suitable supply of singular terms here is that the simpler sentences just mentioned are often substitution-instances of the original ones with respect to certain particular kinds of singular terms (constants).

There are of course types of sentences whose truth-conditions cannot be reduced further in this way. This is the case with atomic sentences and identities. Discarding existential presuppositions adds a new class of such irreducible sentences, viz. the Quinean sentences of the form (48). (I shall not discuss here what kind of semantics is appropriate to them.) Now what happens when uniqueness presuppositions are given up – or, rather, replaced by explicitly formulated uniqueness premises – is that a further class of such irreducible sentences is created. These are precisely the sentences (formulas) of form (22) (or, more generally, of form (24)). Thus the main question which my treatment of modal logics leaves without a sufficiently explicit discussion is the question as to what the truth of these sentences 'really' amounts to.

A partial answer is nevertheless implicit in the above discussion. The intuitive idea on which this discussion is based is the following. Each free singular term picks out a member (an individual or perhaps rather a particular 'stage' or 'manifestation' of an individual) from each possible world we are considering. (I am disregarding the possible emptiness of singular terms here, if only in order to simplify my discussion.) However, the individuals so picked out need not be identical (i.e. they need not be 'manifestations' of the same individual in all these worlds). Only some free singular terms always pick out the same individual. They are the ones that satisfy the appropriate uniqueness conditions (22) (or (24)). In order for this to be an objectively defined notion and in order to speak of the totality of individuals which can in this way manifest themselves in different possible worlds, we must assume that we are given a particular objectively determined set of functions each of which picks from all the appropriate possible worlds the manifestation of *one and the same* individual. These functions, in a sense, are thus the real individuals we are talking about in our sentences, while the members of the several possible worlds are better thought of as so many roles that those individuals may play. In formulating truth-conditions for sentences in which we quantify over individuals, we must speak of the existence of suitable 'individuating functions' of the kind just mentioned. However, if we assume that for each such function there exists a singular term picking out just the several values of this function from those possible worlds we are considering, then we can in fact formulate the truth-conditions by reference to the existence of such singular terms. These exceptionally well-behaved terms will be characterized by the fact that they satisfy the appropriate uniqueness conditions (22) or (24). Thus we are inevitably led to the precise conditions ($C.U_m$) and ($C.E_m$) given above, re-interpreted as truth-conditions for quantified sentences in modal contexts. In this way we can see what kind of semantics goes together with my semi-semantical treatment of modality. It may be that my conditions can be viewed as rules of disproof rather than semantical conditions proper. However, it is very easy to see what semantical counterparts they have.

It must be admitted, however, that for some other purposes a usual semantical approach is more straightforward. Although conditions on model sets and model systems are usually obvious (when acceptable), it is not always equally clear that we have exhausted by their means all the assumptions we have to make in this area. In fact, a moment's reflexion shows that the conditions so far recorded are yet insufficient to capture all the semantical principles we are trying to codify. Apart from the treatment of bound individual variables as subscripts to modal operators, there are at least two kinds of assumptions that remain to be made. One of them is obvious, and merely brings out the possibility of bearing one and the same trans world lines of cross-identity from the point of view of different model sets:

(C. ind*) If

(*) $\quad$ '$(Ex)\,[N^{n_1}(x = b)\ \&\ N^{n_2}(x = b)\ \&\cdots]$' $\in \mu \in \Omega$

and if $\lambda \in \Omega$ is an alternative to μ, then

(**) $$\text{`}(Ex)\,[N^{n_1-1}(x = b)\ \&\ N^{n_2-1}(x = b)\ \&\cdots]\text{'} \in \lambda$$

for $n_i > 1$. (If $n_i = 0$ or $n_i = 1$ for some i, the corresponding conjunct is omitted from (**).)

The need of the other addition to our conditions is brought out by the observation that so far our conditions do not e.g. make the following implication valid:

$$(Ex)\,K_a(b = c\ \&\ K_b p) \supset (Ex)\,K_a(b = c\ \&\ K_c p).$$

The example shows that in the presence of identities their effect on the sentences that express our uniqueness presuppositions (i.e. on (22) and (24)) will have to be taken into account. This does not happen automatically, and these identities have to be taken into account because alternatives to a given world depend merely on the objective identity of its different inhabitants, not on how they are referred to. The best way of doing so seems to me to carry out suitable preliminary simplifications before applying our conditions. I shall not try to formulate the details of these preliminary simplifications here, since the main idea (and its application to many particular cases) is obvious enough. It is important to be aware of the need of further work here, however.

XV. OUR SEMANTICS IS REFERENTIAL

Perhaps the most remarkable feature of this semantics is that one does not quantify over arbitrary functions (or partial functions) that pick out a member from the domain of each possible world (or from some such domains). What one quantifies over is the totality of those functions that pick out *the same* individual from the domains of the different possible worlds (or from some of them). Arbitrary functions of the former kind are essentially what many philosophers call individual concepts, while the latter, narrower set of 'individuating functions' essentially represents the totality of the well-defined individuals we can speak of. Thus the ontology of our semantics, indicated by the ranges of the quantifiers we need, is essentially an ontology of ordinary individuals. The main reason why we have to conceive of our individuals as functions is the obvious fact of our conceptual life that our individuals are not determined for one possible course of events or for one particular moment of time only, but can appear in different roles ('embodiments', 'manifestations', or whatever word you want to use) under several of them. For this reason, to speak of an individual is to speak of its different 'embodiments' in different 'possible worlds', which in turn is but to speak of the function which serves to identify these 'embodiments' as manifestations of *one and the same* individual. Thus our semantics is in a very precise sense referential. The crucial entities we need are precisely the ordinary objects to which singular terms refer, and no quantification over 'meanings' is needed. (The *only* novelty is that these objects are considered as potential members of more than one course of events or state of affairs.) We have thus reached an essentially referential semantics.[20] This is all the more remarkable, it seems to me, in view of the fact that the problems (especially the problem of quantifying into modal contexts) which led us to our present treatment are precisely the problems for the treatment of which non-referential notions such as individual concepts, '*Sinne*', etc. were initially introduced. In a fairly strong sense, we have thus eliminated the need of such notions. (Admittedly, some further questions may still persist, for instance questions pertaining to the nature of individuating functions actually used in our ordinary discourse. I shall by-pass them here, although they certainly need further attention.)

In my semi-semantical treatment, this referential character of our theory is signalled by the fact that in $(C.U_m)$ and $(C.E_m)$ the singular terms of whose existence or non-existence we had to speak were precisely those satisfying the uniqueness conditions (24), i.e. the singular terms which specify a real (unique, well-defined) individual. I have already indicated why we can speak in conditions like $(C.U_m)$ and $(C.E_m)$ of the existence of suitable singular terms instead of speaking of the existence of the individuating functions (= 'real' individuals defined for several different possible worlds), which of course is what in the last analysis is involved in the semantics of modality. I have simply assumed that there is a term correlated with each such individuating function and doing the same job of picking out the different incarnations of the same individual.

There may also be some differences, however, between our treatment and the more explicitly semantical discussions of modality that have actually been given. Certain observations in any case seem easier to make within my framework than in some others.

XVI. FURTHER REMARKS. THE RELATIVITY OF THE NOTION OF INDIVIDUAL

It is in my opinion a remarkable fact that essentially the *only* changes in the deductive relationships among one's formulas necessitated by the new semantics are the ones we have carried out by replacing (C.U) and (C.E) by ($C.U_m$) and ($C.E_m$), respectively. Essentially the *only* change needed is therefore to make formulas of the form (22) (or (24)) logically independent of simpler formulas (e.g. of their own substitution-instances). This insight, it seems to me, emerges more readily from my treatment than from some of the competing ones.

Another suggestion which can be elicited from our discussion is that one's notion of an individual is, in a certain sense, relative to the context of discussion. This is brought out by the fact that the formulas (22) and (24) which serve to guarantee that the singular term '*b*' behaves like a name of a genuine individual are relative to a modal profile. In this respect, I find some of the recent semantical treatments of modality far too absolutistic. Normally, we are not interested in the very long 'trans world heir lines' that pick out the same individual from all sorts of possible worlds. Very often, the only things we are interested in are fairly short bits of these lines, and the only quantification that we really need in such circumstances is quantification over these bits. This is the ultimate reason why in the extreme case of quantification in non-modal logic we do not have to worry about cross-world identifications (i.e. about the roles that actually existing individuals may play in other possible worlds) at all. What precisely the uniqueness requirements are that we have to take into account are formulated more readily in my semi-semantical approach than in ordinary semantical theories.

As was already indicated, an extreme form of this relativity of our notion of an individual is in effect the parallelism of existential presuppositions and uniqueness presuppositions. Only when the relativity I am pleading for is acknowledged can we appreciate the important connection which is signalled by the title of my paper and which is expressed by the slogan that modal logics are in the last analysis but so many 'free' logics.

It can also be seen that some of the assumptions we have made are in effect assumptions concerning the behavior of the lines of cross-identification ('world lines' formed by the different embodiments of one and the same individual in different worlds). For instance, $(C.ind =_0)$ says in effect that such a trans world heir line never branches (splits) when you move from a possible world to its alternatives, however distant. This assumption is not made in all current semantical systems of modal logic, although it has been vigorously defended by some philosophers of logic, notably by Sleigh.[21] Here we can again see what the semantical counterparts of our assumptions are.

We can also see that they will at least partly justify my earlier statement that Quine has not put his finger quite on the right spot in emphasizing the role of the substitutivity of identity. Interpreted in the way we have done (as an assumption of the parity of identical *individuals*), it is a condition that insures that our concept of an individual behaves in certain desirable nice ways (in that individuals do not 'branch'), rather than an indispensable condition that our concept of an individual must in any case satisfy. (The really essential requirements are those codified by $(C.U_m)$ and $(C.E_m)$.) It seems to me that most of our modal notions (e.g. epistemic modalities) satisfy $(C.ind =)$, i.e. behave in these nice ways, but I do not see anything really unique in this particular mode of well-behavedness. It does not seem much more desirable than the converse mode of smooth behavior, which can be described as the impossibility of merging when one goes from a possible world to its alternatives. Yet for most modalities as they are actually used merging seems to me impossible to rule out. (Suppose, for instance, that you have a correct belief as to who or what *a* is, and a similarly correct belief as to who or what *b* is. If the two are in fact different, does it necessarily follow that you must *believe* that they are different? I do not see that this follows at all.)

It must be admitted, however, that there is one fairly strong general reason for ruling out branching in the way Quine has in effect advocated (if I have interpreted him correctly). Earlier, I mentioned the extremely interesting and useful distinction between what can be said of the several references of a term in the different possible worlds we are considering (e.g. of the next president of the United States, 'whoever he is or may be') and between what is said of the individual who in fact (in the actual world) is referred to by a term (e.g. of the man who in fact will be the next president). If we allow branching, the last-mentioned individual is of course not uniquely determined. Then the whole distinction becomes largely inapplicable.

The fact that we can easily understand the distinction and can use it to explicate successfully ambiguities which we feel really are there in our ordinary usage suggests very strongly that the kind of branching we have been discussing is tacitly ruled out in our conceptual system – at least in most circumstances. Hence Quine seems to have after all good reasons for his position, at least in so far as our actual conceptual system is concerned. The naturalness and philosophical interest of the distinction can perhaps be made more obvious by pointing out that to all practical purposes it amounts to the old distinction between modalities *de dicto* and modalities *de re* which was one of the most interesting and useful conceptual tools of the scholastic philosophers.

A closer look at the conditions (C.ind$=_0$) and (C.ind$=$E) in terms of the 'world lines' that our individuating functions define will perhaps enable us to see more clearly what these conditions amount to and what their justification may be. In (C.ind$=_0$) we are considering two 'world lines' both of which are defined for the same selection of possible worlds and which intersect in the actual world. The condition says that these world lines coincide in all the possible worlds in which they were assumed to be defined.

In (C.ind$=$E) we are dealing with two world lines which are defined on partly different classes of possible worlds (which both include the actual one) and which again intersect in the actual world. The condition says that these two world lines can be combined into the world line of one and the same individual.

In both cases, the required behavior of 'world lines' is such as we clearly would like our notion of individual to exhibit. In this sense, there is a great deal to be said for them. Whether it is realistic to assume that we can actually have as nicely defined a notion of individual in the presence of each important modal notion is a question which cannot be adequately discussed here. Nor can it be disposed of by bland assertions to the effect that without those conditions one cannot 'understand' or 'make sense of' quantification into modal contexts. Our semi-semantical treatment already gives us hints as to what the sense would be. Nevertheless, there are good reasons – especially those derived from the successful applications of the *de dicto* – *de re* distinctions – to suggest that in most cases the assumptions are applicable to most of our own modal concepts.

XVII. WORLD LINES CANNOT ALWAYS BE CONTINUED

This problem is connected with another aspect of our approach which at first sight might seem disconcerting. It may seem strange that certain sentences of the following form are *not* always logically true:

(49) $(Ex)p \supset (Ex)(p \,\&\, q)$

where q 'seems' to follow easily from p in the sense that the statement $p(a/x) \,\&\, \sim q(a/x)$ is inconsistent when a is a new individual constant. The technical reason is clear enough. Part of a counter-example to (49) would look like this:

(50) $(Ex)p \in \mu \in \Omega$

(51) $(Ux)(\sim p \vee q) \in \mu$

(52) $p(a/x) \in \mu$

(53) '$Q_p(a)$' $\in \mu$.

Here '$Q_p(x)$' is the uniqueness premise which goes together with the modal profile of p with respect to 'x'. Here (52)–(53) of course follow from (50) by (C.E$_q$). The only further conclusion that can be drawn here is

(54) $[\sim Q_{p\&q}(a) \vee \sim q(a/x)] \in \mu$

(from (51) by (C.U$_q$)). If we could rule out the possibility that

(55) '$\sim Q_{p\&q}(a)$' $\in \mu$

we could produce an inconsistency, for then we would have

(56) $\sim q(a/x) \in \mu$

by (C.$\vee$). However, there is nothing to rule out (55), provided only that the uniqueness requirement expressed by '$Q_{p\&q}(x)$' is stronger than that expressed by '$Q_p(x)$'. (The only way of ruling out (55) seems to make (53) imply that '$Q_{p\&q}(a)$' $\in \mu$.) Hence a counter-example cannot be ruled out, and (49) need not be logically true.

Does this go to show that our treatment of modality is unnatural? In my opinion it does nothing of the sort, however surprising and disconcerting this phenomenon might first appear. Rather, it gives us a chance of characterizing interesting differences between different kinds of modal notions.

The semantical situation that goes together with the failure of the logical truth of (49) is not hard to fathom. The relativization of uniqueness presuppositions means that normally we are not quantifying over the whole long trans world heir lines that constitute all that can be said of our individuals in objective terms, but rather quantifying over assorted bits and pieces of such heir lines.

If each such bit of an heir line could always be extended arbitrarily far to further possible worlds, this would not make any difference. But assuming this would mean assuming further interconnections between the different uniqueness conditions. These assumptions amount to assuming the validity (logical truth) of sentences of the following form:

(57) $\text{‘}(Ux)\,[Q_1(x) \supset (Ey)\,(x = y \,\&\, Q_2(y))]\text{’}$

for some (or maybe all) the different kinds of uniqueness premises ‘Q_1’, ‘Q_2’. These very same assumptions are, as our example (50)–(56) above suggests, just what is needed to show such implications as (49) to be logically true.

Such assumptions as (57) might look very tempting. This temptation is probably due to the fact that statements of form (57) are in fact logically true *for logical necessity* and perhaps also for physical (natural) necessity. However, there is no reason to assume the validity of (57) for most of the other modal notions (in the wide sense of the word), including propositional attitudes. In fact, an individual might e.g. be perfectly well defined as far as the belief-worlds of some specified person (say the person referred to by ‘a’) are concerned (and hence give rise to nice trans world heir lines connecting these worlds), and yet fail to be uniquely determined as far as somebody else’s beliefs are concerned – which means that the heir lines in question cannot be extended to *his* ‘belief worlds’ (worlds compatible with everything he believes). The same holds obviously for many other propositional attitudes.

An example will hopefully convince the reader of the relevance of what I just said. An instance of (57) might be

(58) $\text{‘}(Ux)\,[(Ey)\,B_a(y = x) \supset (Ez)\,(z = x \,\&\, (Ey)\,B_a\,B_b(y = z))]\text{’}$

which would say (roughly) that whenever the bearer of ‘a’ has an opinion concerning the identity of an individual, he believes that the person referred to by 'b' also has such an opinion. This, of course, is clearly false in most cases.

The presence of such further assumptions as the transitivity and reflexivity (of the alternativeness relation which goes together with a modal notion) greatly reduces the number of possible assumptions of form (57) to be accepted or rejected. But even then one can see that these assumptions are generally unacceptable. For instance, for a discussion of a particular man's knowledge (let him be referred to by 'a'), one of the few relevant assumptions of form (55) would be expressed by

(59) $$\text{'}(Ux)\,[(Ey)\,(y = x) \supset (Ez)\,(z = x \;\&\; (Ey)\,K_a(y = z))]\text{'}.$$

What this says is that the man referred to by 'a' knows of each actually existing individual who or what it is. This is obviously false in all interesting applications.

Thus the failure of statements of form (49) to be logically true is not disconcerting at all. Instead, it points to an interesting general conceptual fact. Such statements as (49) and (57) fail to be logically true because what counts as an individual varies from one man and from one attitude to another, and is not determined by the set of actually existing individuals. Thus the failure of an instance of (49) or (57) for a given notion seems to be an indication of the intentional (psychological) character of the notion. In contrast to such intentional notions as belief, non-intentional modalities like logical necessity seem to make them logically true.

If assumptions like (57) are combined with (C.ind=) and (C.ind=E), all uniqueness premises will coincide with each other and with the existence premise '$(Ex)(x=b)$'. The situation then becomes rather trivial. This fact may perhaps be used as an argument against the interest of logical modalities as an object of semantical study compared e.g. with propositional attitudes. More generally, in this way we can see, not just the technical possibility of relativizing one's uniqueness assumptions, but some of the insights gained by so doing – and the necessity of such a course in the case of propositional attitudes.

XVIII. CONTRA LOGICAL MODALITIES

This line of thought can in fact be turned into a more serious criticism of logical modalities than a comment on their relatively trivial logical behavior. We have not yet said anything about the ways in which the identifying functions can be defined which enable us to speak of the *same* individual appearing in several different possible worlds. Nor can anything like a satisfactory discussion be given within the confines of one essay. However, it is clear what sorts of criteria are used here: they turn on the similarities between different possible worlds and on regularities obtaining in each of the possible worlds we have to consider (for instance, on the continuity of our individuals with respect to space and time). If this is not immediately clear to a reader, we can invite him to consider what it is that makes it possible for him to speak of more or less the same set of individuals all the time when discussing what possible courses of events might materialize between today and next week, as far as his beliefs are concerned. If he did not believe in the spatial and temporal continuity of persons, chairs and molecules, he might have some difficulty in justifying his talk of the *same* individuals independent of the particular course of events he happens to be considering.

If this is the case, relativization of world lines is a dire necessity. For if we want to extend them indefinitely, we might run into possible worlds that simply are so irregular that our customary methods of cross-identifying individuals (=telling whether the inhabitants of different possible worlds are or are not the same) may simply fail.

In the case of most applications of propositional attitudes, this is avoided because the possible worlds that are in fact compatible with people's propositional attitudes are fairly regular and pretty similar to each other. However, it seems to me that even here the applicability of our semantical concepts depends on assumptions concerning the degree of realism in people's propositional attitudes. But in the case of logical modalities (logical and analytical possibility and necessity) the different worlds we (so to speak *per definitionem*) have to consider can be so irregular and dissimilar that all the methods of cross-identification that are used in our native conceptual system are bound to fail. If so, we cannot quantify into contexts governed by words for such logical modalities, for such quantification depends essentially on criteria of cross-identification (individuating functions, world lines).

If so, Quine turns out to have been right in his suspicion of quantified modal logic in the narrow sense of the word as quantification theory plus *logical* modalities. However, there do not seem to be any objections to a theory of propositional attitudes *cum* quantification. In fact, it is only by developing a satisfactory semantical theory for languages which embody both these elements that the deep true reasons for rejecting a quantified logic of logical modalities finally begin to emerge.

REFERENCES

[1] The Irvine Colloquium in May 1968.

[2] For further remarks on this point, see my paper, 'Logic and Philosophy' in *Contemporary Philosophy – La Philosophie Contemporaine*, vol. I (ed. by R. Klibansky), Florence 1968.

[3] 'Language-Games for Quantifiers', *American Philosophical Quarterly, Monograph Series*, no. 2 (1968): Studies in Logical Theory, pp. 46–72.

[4] On this subject, see my paper 'On the Logic of Existence and Necessity I: Existence', *The Monist* **50** (1966) 55–76. The present paper includes much of the material which I intended to include in the second part of that earlier paper.

[5] There will be some overlap with my discussion note 'Individuals, Possible Worlds, and Epistemic Logic', *Noûs* **1** (1967) 33–62.

[6] See e.g. 'Knowledge, Identity, and Existence', *Theoria* **33** (1967) 1–27; 'Interpretation of Quantifiers' in *Logic, Methodology, and Philosophy of Science III, Proceedings of the 1967 International Congress* (ed. by B. van Rootselaar and J. F. Staal), Amsterdam 1968, pp. 435–444; also 'Quine on Modality', *Synthese* **19** (1968–69) 147–157.

[7] In order to prove this, it suffices to show that whenever Ω is a model system which satisfies the earlier conditions, we can adjoin new formulas to its members so as to obtain a new model system Ω' which in addition to the earlier conditions also satisfies (C.N=). (Then the same sets of formulas will be satisfiable in either case.) This can be accomplished as follows: whenever $\mu \in \Omega$, adjoin to μ all formulas p such that for some finite sequence of formulas $p_0 = p, p_1, p_2, \ldots, p_k$ and some suitable singular terms 'a_1', 'b_1', 'a_2', 'b_2',..., 'a_k', 'b_k' (not necessarily different), '$N^{n_i}(a_i = b_i)$' $\in \mu$ or '$N^{n_i}(a_i = b_i)$' $= p_j$ for $j < i (i = 1, \ldots k)$ and p_i and p_{i-1} are like except that a_i and b_i have been exchanged at some place or places where they occur in the scope of precisely n_i modal operators. That Ω' so constructed satisfies (C.N =) is immediately obvious. That it satisfies the other conditions can be proved by induction on the number of symbols '&', '$\vee$', 'E', 'U', 'N', 'M'.

[8] See e.g. my paper, 'Modality and Quantification', *Theoria* **27** (1961) 119–128.

[9] Admittedly Quine also frequently mentions the failure of existential generalization as an indication of trouble in quantified modal logic. The impression he leaves, however, is that this is just another symptom of one and the same illness. We shall soon see that the question of the validity of the substitutivity of identity is largely independent of those changes in the quantifier conditions (C.E) and (C.U) which determine the fate of existential generalization.

See e.g. W. V. Quine, *From a Logical Point of View*, 2nd ed., Cambridge, Mass., 1961, pp. 139–159; *The Ways of Paradox*, New York 1966, pp. 156–182; Dagfinn Føllesdal, papers referred to in note 6 above.

[10] Alternatively, we may express the last part of this condition as follows: ... and if '$Q^{n_1, n_2, \cdots}(b)$' $\in \mu$, then $p(b/x) \in \mu$.

[11] Special cases of this argument were given in Jaakko Hintikka, 'On the Logic of Existence and Necessity' (note 4 above) and 'Individuals, Possible Worlds, and Epis-

temic Logic' (note 5 above). In the latter, the generalization presented here was also anticipated.

[12] Again, (C.U1) may be formulated as follows: ... and if '$(Ex)(N^{n_1}(x=b) \& N^{n_2}(x=b) \& \ldots)$' $\in \mu$, then $p(b/x) \in \mu$. Here instead of '$(Ex)(N^{n_1}(x=b) \& N^{n_2}(x=b) \& \ldots)$' we may have any formula obtained from it by the following operations: changing the order of conjunction members and/or identities; replacing the bound variable everywhere by another one.

[13] Here we see especially sharply the difference between questions pertaining to the substitutivity of identity and questions pertaining to existential generalization. In the former, the question is whether two singular terms pick out the same individual in *each* possible world in a certain class of possible worlds (considered alone without regard to the others). In the latter, we are asking whether a given singular term picks out one and the same individual in *all* possible worlds of a certain kind (when they are compared with each other).

[14] See e.g. my paper 'Modality and Quantification' (note 8 above).

[15] The general validity of (26) presupposes that any actually existing individual also exists in all the alternatives to the actual world. The following model system Ω provides a counter-example to (26): Ω consists of μ and v, the latter of which is an alternative to the former. Here

$$\mu = \{(Ex)Np, Np(a/x), (Ex)(x=a), p(a/x), M(Ux) \sim p$$
$$v = \{(Ux) \sim p, p(a/x)\}.$$

We could not have this counter-example, however, if '$(Ex)(x=a)$' $\in \mu$ entailed '$(Ex)(x=a)$' $\in v$, i.e. if we could 'move' an existence assumption concerning a from a possible world to its alternatives.

[16] Thus the elimination of existential presuppositions helps us to dispense with unwanted assumptions concerning the 'transfer' of individuals from a possible world to its alternatives.

[17] This is one of the many places where one is easily misled if one trusts uncritically the superficial suggestions of ordinary language. Surely there are circumstances in which someone knows who is referred to by 'a' is and also knows who is referred to by 'b' is while in reality '$a=b$' is true, apparently without thereby *knowing that the references of* 'a' *and* 'b' *are identical*, contrary to what (C.ind.$=_0$) requires. However, one has to insist here very strongly that in the two cases of a and b, respectively, precisely the same sense (same criteria) of knowing who must be presupposed. This is not the case, it seems to me, in any of the apparent counter-examples that have been offered.

[18] In his paper, 'Some Problems about Belief' *Synthese* **19** (1968–69) 158–177, especially pp. 168–169, Wilfrid Sellars claims in effect that the validity of (C.ind$=_0$) is ruled out by the interpretation of quantifiers which I propose in my *Knowledge and Belief*, Ithaca, N.Y., 1962. This argument completely misconstrues my intended interpretation, however, for reasons I can only guess at, and hence fails to have any relevance here. Although (C.ind$=_0$) was not mentioned in *Knowledge and Belief*, there is nothing there that rules this condition out for syntactical or for semantical reasons. Nor is there anything in *Knowledge and Belief* that is affected by the adjunction of this new condition.

[19] A few additional comments are presented in my paper, 'Semantics for Propositional Attitudes' in *Philosophical Logic* (ed. by J. W. Davis, D. J. Hockney and W. K. Wilson), D. Reidel Publishing Company, Dordrecht 1969.

[20] Cf 'Semantics for Propositional Attitudes' (note 19 above).

[21] See R. Sleigh, 'On Quantifying into Epistemic Contexts', *Noûs* **1** (1967) 23–32.

RICHMOND H. THOMASON

SOME COMPLETENESS RESULTS FOR MODAL PREDICATE CALCULI*

I. INTRODUCTION

Two systems of first-order predicate calculus with identity, one of them with definite descriptions, will be formulated in this paper along with semantic interpretations, and then shown strongly complete by methods similar to those of Henkin [3]. These systems, **Q1** and **Q3**,[1] are generalizations of the systems presented in Kripke [6] and [8], respectively.[2] An informal and philosophical account of **Q1** and **Q3** can be found in [11], together with a historical note concerning the development of the systems and their interpretation.

It is known that a semantically complete interpretation of a system with **S4**-type modality also produces a complete interpretation of the corresponding intuitionistic system. This result for intuitionistic logic has already appeared (again following the lead of Kripke, in [9]) in Thomason [12]. In presenting the syntax and semantic interpretation of **Q1** and **Q3** below, I have used the same format as in the last-named article.

The methods of proof which we will use below apply generally to many different sorts of modality: in particular, to alethic and deontic versions of **S4** and **S5**, von Wright's **M**, and the 'Brouwersche' **B**. But to simplify our presentation, we confine ourselves below to systems which involve the modality of alethic **S4**, leaving it to the reader to generalize the arguments to other modalities. See reference 7 in this connection.

II. MORPHOLOGY

A *morphology* **M** for the first-order modal predicate calculus with identity is a structure made up of the following (disjoint) components:

(1) An infinite well-ordered set V_M of objects called *individual variables*;
(2) A well-ordered set C_M of objects called *individual constants*;
(3) For each nonnegative integer i, a well-ordered set P^i_M of objects called *i-ary predicate letters.*

K. Lambert (ed.), Philosophical Problems in Logic.

Let $\supset$, $\sim$, $\Box$,), (, and $=$ be objects not in any of the P^i_M, or in V_M or C_M. These seven objects (or *logical symbols*), together with the members of V_M, C_M, and the P^i_M, comprise the symbols of **M**. The set T_M of *terms* of **M** is $C_M \cup V_M$; the set W_M of formulas of **M** consists of certain finite strings of symbols of **M**, and is defined in the usual way. Using the orderings posited in (1)–(3) above, W_M can easily be well-ordered. (*Remark*: we will frequently suppress mention of the morphology in cases where no confusion can result from doing so. We will assume in this paper that for all morphologies **M**, the sets V_M, C_M, P^i_M – and hence the set W_M – are at most denumerable, and are ordered alphabetically by the positive integers. The main results of this paper depend on this assumption; see references 4 and 10 in this connection.)

If **M** is a morphology with identity and descriptions, another symbol, $\imath$, is added and T_M and W_M are defined by simultaneous induction. (The inductive clause for terms is that $\imath_x A \in T_M$ if $A \in W_M$ and $x \in V_M$.)

Where A is a formula and s and t terms, let As/t be the result of replacing all free occurrences of t in A by occurrences of s – relettering bound variables, if necessary, to avoid rendering the new occurrences of s bound in As/t. And let $As//t$ be any result of replacing various (not necessarily all, or even any) free occurrences of t in A by occurrences of s – again, relettering if necessary.

We will use '$A \vee B$', '$A \wedge B$', '$A \equiv B$', '$\Diamond A$', '$(\exists x)\, A$' and '$A \prec B$' as abbreviations (in our metalanguage) of '$((A \supset B) \supset B)$', '$\sim(A \supset \sim B)$', '$\sim((A \supset B) \supset \sim(B \supset A))$', '$\sim\Box\sim A$', '$\sim(x)\sim A$', and '$\Box(A \supset B)$', respectively. '$Et$' and '$E\Box t$' refer respectively to $(\exists x)\, x = t$ and to $(\exists x)\Box x = t$, where x is the alphabetically first individual variable differing from t, and '$(\exists! x)A$' to $(\exists y)\,(x)\,(A \equiv x = y)$, where y is the alphabetically first individual variable not to occur in A.

III. DEDUCIBILITY IN THE SYSTEM Q1

In **Q1** a deductive structure is imposed on morphologies **M** for the first-order modal predicate calculus with identity (but without descriptions) by closing a set of axioms under certain rules. The axioms are determined by stipulating that any tautology is an axiom, as well as any instance of the following eight schemes.[3]

A1. $\square(A \supset B) \supset . \square A \supset \square B$
A2. $\square A \supset A$
A3. $\square A \supset \square\square A$
A4. $(x)A \supset A^t/x$, where t is any term
A5. $s = s$
A6. $s = t \supset . A \supset A^s//t$
A7. $(x)\square A \supset \square (x)A$
A8. $\Diamond s = t \supset \square s = t.$

The rules of proof in **Q1** are as follows.

R1. $\dfrac{A \qquad A \supset B}{B}$

R2. $\dfrac{A}{\square A}$

R3. $\dfrac{A \supset B}{A \supset (x)B}$ where x is not free in A.

Deducibility in **Q1** may be defined in much the same way as in Montague and Henkin [10]. Call a member A_i of a sequence $A_1, \ldots, A_n$ of formulas **Q1**-*categorical* in that sequence if some subsequence of $A_1, \ldots, A_i$ is a proof in **Q1** of A_i, and let a sequence $B_1, \ldots, B_k$ be a **Q1**-*derivation* of B_k from a set Γ of formulas if for all i, $1 \leqslant i \leqslant k$, B_i is an axiom of **Q1** or a member of Γ, or follows from previous members of the sequence by R1, or is categorical in the sequence by R2 or R3. And '$\Gamma \vdash_1 A$' means that there is a **Q1**-derivation of A from Γ. Finally, Γ is **Q1**-*consistent* if there is a formula A such that it is not the case that $\Gamma \vdash_1 A$.

For reference in proving metatheorems to come, we record the following facts about **Q1**-deducibility.

T1. If $\Gamma \vdash_1 A$ then $\{\square B / B \in \Gamma\} \vdash_1 \square A$.
T2. $\vdash_1 s = t \supset \square s = t$.

IV. Q1-SATURATION

D1. A subset Γ of $\mathrm{W_M}$ is **Q1-M**-*saturated* (abbreviated 'M-saturated' in this section and in Sections V and VI, below) if it meets the following three conditions:

(1) Γ is **Q1**-consistent;

(2) For all $A \in W_M$, $A \in \Gamma$ or $\sim A \in \Gamma$;

(3) For all $A \in W_M$ and $x \in V_M$, $(x) A \in \Gamma$ if $A^t/x \in \Gamma$ for all $t \in T_M$.

We will use bold face Greek capitals to range over saturated sets.

By a **Q1**-*ω-extension* of a morphology **M** (abbreviated 'ω-extension' in this section and in Section VI) we understand a morphology **M′** like **M** except that $C_{M'} = C_M \cup \{c_1, c_2, \ldots\}$, where $c_1, c_2, \ldots$ are symbols foreign to **M**.

L1. Every **Q1**-consistent subset Γ of W_M has an **M′**-saturated extension $\boldsymbol{\Gamma}$, where **M′** is any ω-extension of **M**.

The demonstration of this lemma does not differ from that of its classical analogue; all that is needed for its proof are elementary syntactic features of **Q1** and willingness to use the axiom of choice or a like principle. Since every $\boldsymbol{\Gamma}$ is **Q1**-consistent, we can strengthen L1 a bit.

L2. For any $\Gamma \subseteq W_M$ and ω-extension **M′** of **M**, Γ is **Q1**-consistent iff Γ has an **M′**-saturated extension $\boldsymbol{\Gamma}$.

In preparation for our needs in Section VI, below, we establish the following syntactic lemma, which is the crucial step in our proof of the semantic completeness of **Q1**.

L3. Let $\boldsymbol{\Gamma}$ be any **M**-saturated set, let $\Delta_1 \mathscr{R} \Delta_2$ iff $\{A/\Box A \in \Delta_1\} \subseteq \Delta_2$ and let $\mathscr{K}$ be the closure of $\{\boldsymbol{\Gamma}\}$ under $\mathscr{R}$. Then $\mathscr{K}$ satisfies the following condition: for all $\Delta \in \mathscr{K}$ and all $A \in W_M$, if $\Diamond A \in \Delta$ then there is a $\Delta' \in \mathscr{K}$ such that $A \in \Delta'$ and $\Delta \mathscr{R} \Delta'$.

PROOF. Let $\Theta = \{B/\Box B \in \Delta\}$. Now, the set Θ satisfies condition (3) of *D*1, since if $B^t/x \in \Theta$ for all $t \in T_M$, then $\Box B^t/x \in \Delta$ for all $t \in T_M$ and hence $(x) \Box B \in \Delta$. But then, by A7, $\Box (x) B \in \Delta$, so that $(x) B \in \Theta$. Knowing that Θ satisfies condition (3) of D1, it is easy to see that Ξ does, where Ξ is the closure of $\Xi \cup \{A\}$ under $\vdash_1$.

Also Ξ is **Q1**-consistent, since if it were the case that $\Theta \vdash_1 \sim A$, then by T1 we would have $\{\Box B/\Box B \in \Delta\} \vdash_1 \Box \sim A$ and since by assumption $\Diamond A \in \Delta$, Δ would be **Q1**-inconsistent.

The proof which Henkin gives in [3], pp. 3–4, of Theorem 3 of that paper establishes for the classical predicate calculus (without identity) that every consistent subset of W_M satisfying condition (3) of D1 has an **M**-saturated extension, and no changes whatsoever are needed to make this argument work also for **Q1**.[4] Applying this result to Ξ we obtain the desired **M**-saturated extension $\boldsymbol{\Gamma}$ of $\Theta \cup \{A\}$.

V. SEMANTICS OF Q1 [5]

A **Q1-S4**-*model structure* (in the present paper, abbreviated '**Q1**ms') is a triple $\langle \mathscr{K}, \mathscr{R}, \mathscr{D} \rangle$,where $\mathscr{K}$ is a nonempty set, $\mathscr{R}$ a binary reflexive and transitive relation on $\mathscr{D}$, and $\mathscr{D}$ a non-empty [6] domain.

A **Q1**-*interpretation* I of a morphology **M** on a **Q1**ms $\langle \mathscr{K}, \mathscr{R}, \mathscr{D} \rangle$ is a function which assigns:

(1) To each $x \in V_{\mathbf{M}}$ a member $I(x)$ of $\mathscr{D}$;
(2) To each $c \in C_{\mathbf{M}}$ a member $I(c)$ of $\mathscr{D}$;
(3) To each $P^0 \in P^0_{\mathbf{M}}$ a value $I(P^0)$ in $\{T, F\}$, and to each $P^i \in P^i_{\mathbf{M}}$ $(i > 0)$ a subset $I_\alpha(P^i)$, for each $\alpha \in \mathscr{K}$, of the cartesian product $\mathscr{D}^i$.

Where $d \in \mathscr{D}$, I^d/x is to be the interpretation differing (if at all) from I only in assigning d to x.

The truth-value $I_\alpha(A)$ of A in α under a **Q1**-interpretation I on a **Q1**ms $\langle \mathscr{K}, \mathscr{R}, \mathscr{D} \rangle$ (where $\alpha \in \mathscr{K}$), is defined inductively as follows.

(1) $I_\alpha(Pt_1 \dots t_n) = T$ if $\langle I(t_1), \dots, I(t_n) \rangle \in I_\alpha(P)$,
$I_\alpha(Pt_1 \dots t_n) = F$ otherwise;
(2) $I_\alpha(s = t) = T$ if $I(s) = I(t)$,
$I_\alpha(s = t) = F$ otherwise;
(3) $I_\alpha(A \supset B) = T$ if $I_\alpha(A) = F$ or $I_\alpha(B) = T$,
$I_\alpha(A \supset B) = F$ otherwise;
(4) $I_\alpha(\sim A) = T$ if $I_\alpha(A) = F$,
$I_\alpha(\sim A) = F$ otherwise;
(5) $I_\alpha(\Box A) = T$ if for all $\beta \in \mathscr{K}$ such that $\alpha \mathscr{R} \beta$, $I_\beta(A) = T$,
$I_\alpha(\Box A) = F$ otherwise;
(6) $I_\alpha((x)A) = T$ if for all $d \in \mathscr{D}$, $I^d/x_\alpha(A) = T$,
$I_\alpha((x)A) = F$ otherwise.

The following lemma concerning the relationship of syntactic and semantic substitution is readily proved by induction on the complexity of A.

L4. $I_\alpha(A^t/x) = I^{I(t)}/x_\alpha(A)$.

An interpretation I on a **Q1**ms $\langle \mathscr{K}, \mathscr{R}, \mathscr{D} \rangle$ *simultaneously satisfies* Γ in α if $I_\alpha(A) = T$ for all $A \in \Gamma$. Where $\Gamma \subseteq W_{\mathbf{M}}$, Γ is *simultaneously* **Q1**-*satisfiable* if there is some **Q1**ms $\langle \mathscr{K}, \mathscr{R}, \mathscr{D} \rangle$, interpretation I of **M** on $\langle\mathscr{K}, \mathscr{R}, \mathscr{D}\rangle$ and $\alpha \in \mathscr{K}$ such that I simultaneously satisfies Γ in α. A formula A is **Q1**-valid if $\{\sim A\}$ is not simultaneously **Q1**-satisfiable.

L5. Let I be an interpretation of **M** on a **Q1**ms $\langle\mathscr{K}, \mathscr{R}, \mathscr{D}\rangle$ such that for all $\mathrm{d} \in \mathscr{D}$ there is a $t \in \mathrm{T}_{\mathbf{M}}$ such that $\mathrm{I}(t)=\mathrm{d}$, and let $\alpha \in \mathscr{K}$. Then the set $\Gamma=\{A/\mathrm{I}_\alpha(A)=\mathrm{T} \text{ and } A \in \mathrm{W}_{\mathbf{M}}\}$ of formulas of **M** simultaneously **Q1**-satisfied by I in α is **M**-saturated.

PROOF. Conditions (2) and (3) of D1 are met trivially. To establish condition (1), one need only verify that A1–A8 are **Q1**-valid and that R1–R3 preserve **Q1**-validity.

VI. SEMANTIC COMPLETENESS OF Q1

L6. Let $\boldsymbol{\Gamma}$ be **M**-saturated. Then there is an interpretation I of **M** on a **Q1**ms $\langle\mathscr{K}, \mathscr{R}, \mathscr{D}\rangle$ and an $\alpha \in \mathscr{K}$ such that $\boldsymbol{\Gamma}$ is the set of formulas of **M** simultaneously **Q1**-satisfied by I in α.

PROOF. Let $\mathscr{R}$ be as in L3 and let $\mathscr{K}$ be the closure of $\{\boldsymbol{\Gamma}\}$ under $\mathscr{R}$: i.e. $\mathscr{K}$ is the smallest set S such that $\boldsymbol{\Gamma} \in \mathrm{S}$ and for all $\varDelta$ and $\boldsymbol{\Theta}$, if $\varDelta \in \mathrm{S}$ and $\varDelta \mathscr{R} \boldsymbol{\Theta}$ then $\boldsymbol{\Theta} \in \mathrm{S}$. The relation $\simeq$ on $\mathrm{T}_{\mathbf{M}}$ such that $s \simeq t$ iff $s=t \in \boldsymbol{\Gamma}$ is an equivalence relation and hence divides $\mathrm{T}_{\mathbf{M}}$ into disjoint partitions; let $\mathscr{D}$ be a set of representatives, one from each of these partitions, and let $\mathrm{f}(t)$ be the representative of the partition to which t belongs.

The triple $\langle\mathscr{K}, \mathscr{R}, \mathscr{D}\rangle$ is a **Q1**ms; to verify this, we need only check that $\mathscr{R}$ is reflexive and transitive, and this follows at once from A2 and A3.[7]

We now define an interpretation I of **M** on $\langle\mathscr{K}, \mathscr{R}, \mathscr{D}\rangle$, as follows: $\mathrm{I}(t)=\mathrm{f}(t)$; $\mathrm{I}_\varDelta(P^0)=\mathrm{T}$ if $P^0 \in \varDelta$ and $\mathrm{I}_\varDelta(P^0)=\mathrm{F}$ if $P^0 \notin \varDelta$; and where $i>0$, $\mathrm{I}_\varDelta(P^i)=\{\langle \mathrm{f}(t_1),\ldots,\mathrm{f}(t_i)\rangle / P^i t_1 \ldots t_i \in \varDelta\}$.

By induction on the complexity of A, we show that for all $A \in \mathbf{M}$ and $\varDelta \in \mathscr{K}$, $\mathrm{I}_\varDelta(A)=\mathrm{T}$ iff $A \in \varDelta$. The more interesting cases are the following.

CASE 1. A is $P^i t_1 \ldots t_i$. Because of T2 and A8, we have $s \simeq t$ iff $s=t \in \varDelta$ for all $\varDelta \in \mathscr{K}$. Hence the formulas $t_1=\mathrm{f}(t_1), \ldots, t_i=\mathrm{f}(t_i)$ are all in each $\varDelta \in \mathscr{K}$. Therefore by A6, for all $\varDelta \in \mathscr{K}$ we have $A \in \varDelta$ iff $P^i \mathrm{f}(t_1) \ldots \mathrm{f}(t_i) \in \varDelta$. And by definition of I, this iff $\mathrm{I}_\varDelta(A)=\mathrm{T}$.

CASE 2. A is $s=t$. Now, $\mathrm{I}_\varDelta(A)=\mathrm{T}$ iff $\mathrm{I}(s)=\mathrm{I}(t)$. But by definition of I, $\mathrm{I}_\varDelta(s)=\mathrm{I}_\varDelta(t)$ iff $s=t \in \boldsymbol{\Gamma}$, and, as we know, this iff $s=t \in \varDelta$.

CASE 5. A is $\Box B$. Now if $\Box A \in \varDelta$, then by definition of $\mathscr{R}$, $B \in \varDelta'$ for all $\varDelta'$ such that $\varDelta \mathscr{R} \varDelta'$; hence by the hypothesis of induction, $\mathrm{I}_{\varDelta'}(B)=\mathrm{T}$

for all such Δ', and so $I_\Delta(A)=T$. Conversely, if $A \notin \Delta$, then $\Diamond \sim B \in \Delta$ and by L3 there is a $\Delta' \in \mathscr{K}$ such that $\Delta \mathscr{R} \Delta'$ and $\sim B \in \Delta'$; hence $B \notin \Delta'$. By the hypothesis of induction, $I_{\Delta'}(B)=F$, and so $I_\Delta(A)=F$.

CASE 6. A is $(x)B$. By condition (3) of D1, $A \in \Delta$ iff for all $t \in T_M$, $I_\Delta(Bt/x)=T$. Applying L4, we see this is equivalent to the condition that for all $t \in T_M$, $I^{I(t)}/x_\Delta(B)=T$ (i.e. $I^{f(t)}/x_\Delta(B)=T$). And, since $\mathscr{D}=\{f(t)/ t \in T_M\}$, this holds iff $I_\Delta(A)=T$.

We have now shown that for all $A \in W_M$ and $\Delta \in \mathscr{K}$, $I_\Delta(A)=T$ iff $A \in \Delta$; hence, in particular, $\boldsymbol{\Gamma}=\{A/I_{\boldsymbol{\Gamma}}(A)=T \text{ and } A \in W_M\}$, which was to be proved.

L7. A set Γ is **M**-saturated iff there exists a **Q1**ms $\langle \mathscr{C}, \mathscr{R}, \mathscr{D}\rangle$, an interpretation I of **M** on $\langle \mathscr{K}, \mathscr{R}, \mathscr{D}\rangle$ and an $\alpha \in \mathscr{K}$ such that for all $d \in \mathscr{D}$ there is a $t \in T_M$ such that $I(t)=d$, and $\Gamma=\{A/I_\alpha(A)=T\}$.

PROOF. Since the interpretation I defined in the proof of L6 is such that for all $d \in \mathscr{D}$ there is a $t \in T_M$ such that $I(t)=d$, L5 and the proof of L6 together yield the desired result.

L8. Let **M**′ be an ω-extension of **M**, and Γ a subset of **M**. Then Γ is simultaneously **Q1**-satisfiable iff Γ has an **M**′-saturated extension $\boldsymbol{\Gamma}$.

PROOF. Suppose first that Γ has an **M**′-saturated extension $\boldsymbol{\Gamma}$; by L7, $\boldsymbol{\Gamma}$ is simultaneously **Q1**-satisfiable, and hence, so is Γ. Conversely, if Γ is simultaneously **Q1**-satisfiable then by L5, Γ is a subset of a **Q1**-consistent set and hence itself is **Q1**-consistent. Then by L1, Γ has an **M**-saturated extension $\boldsymbol{\Gamma}$.

T1. (Strong semantic completeness of **Q1**). A subset Γ of W_M is **Q1**-consistent iff Γ is **Q1**-satisfiable.

PROOF. Let **M**′ be an ω-extension of **M**. By L2, a subset Γ of W_M is **Q1**-consistent iff Γ has an **M**′-saturated extension $\boldsymbol{\Gamma}$. But in view of L8, Γ has an **M**′-saturated extension $\boldsymbol{\Gamma}$ iff Γ is simultaneously **Q1**-satisfiable.

As usual, T1 yields as corollary the weak semantic completeness of **Q1**.

T2. For all formulas A of **M**, A is **Q1**-valid iff $\vdash_1 A$.

This concludes our treatment of the system **Q1**; we proceed now to an account of **Q3**.

VII. DEDUCIBILITY IN THE SYSTEM Q3

In the system **Q3**, definite descriptions are primitive; therefore, whenever we use the term 'morphology' below, we understand 'morphology with identity and descriptions'. Any tautology is an axiom of **Q3**, as well as any instance of the following twelve schemes.

A1. $\Box(A \supset B) \supset . \Box A \supset \Box B$

A2. $\Box A \supset A$

A3. $\Box A \supset \Box\Box A$

A4′. $(x)A \supset . \mathrm{E}\Box t \supset A^t/x$, where t is any term

A5′. $(x)(\mathrm{E}x \supset A) \supset (x)A$

A6′. $(\exists x)\,\mathrm{E}x$

A7′. $s = s$

A8′. $s = t \supset . A \supset A^s//t$, where no occurrence of t in A that is replaced by s falls within the scope of a modal operator

A9′. $\mathrm{E}\,\iota_x A \supset (\exists!x)A$

A10′. $(y)((x)(A \equiv x = y) \supset y = \iota_x A)$

A11′. $x = y \supset \Box x = y$, where x and y are individual variables

A12′. $\Diamond x = y \supset x = y$, where x and y are individual variables.

The rules of proof of **Q3** are as follows.[8]

R1. $\dfrac{A \qquad A \supset B}{B}$

R2. $\dfrac{A}{\Box A}$

R3. $\dfrac{A \supset B}{A \supset (x)B}$, where x is not free in A

R4. $\dfrac{A \supset \Box B}{A \supset \Box(x)B}$, where x is not free in A

R5. $\dfrac{A \supset . B_1 \prec . \cdots \prec . B_n \prec \Box C}{A \supset . B_1 \prec . \cdots \prec . B_n \prec \Box(x)C}$, where x is not free in A, $B_1, \ldots$, or B_n

R6. $\dfrac{A \supset \sim t = x}{\sim A}$ where x is not free in A or in t

R7. $\dfrac{A \supset . B_1 \prec . \cdots \prec . B_n \prec \sim t = x}{A \supset . B_1 \prec . \cdots \prec . \Box \sim B_n}$, where x is not free in A, $B_1, \ldots, B_n$, or t.

The definitions of **Q3**-derivability and **Q3**-consistency are carried out as are the analogous definitions in the case of **Q1**. We record here the following facts about **Q3**-derivability.

T3. If $\Gamma \cup \{A^y/x\} \vdash_3 B$, and y is an individual variable not occurring in B or in any member of Γ, then $\Gamma \cup \{(\exists x)A\} \vdash_3 B$.

T4. $\vdash_3 (\exists x)\,(((\exists x)A \supset A) \wedge \mathrm{E}x)$.

T5. If Γ is **Q3**-consistent and $\Diamond(A_1 \wedge \cdots \wedge A_n) \in \Gamma$, then $\{A_1, \ldots, A_n\}$ is **Q3**-consistent.

T6. $\vdash_3 \mathrm{E}x \equiv \mathrm{E}\,\Box\, x$, where x is an individual variable.

T7. $\vdash_3 x = y \supset . A \supset A^x//y$, where x and y are individual variables.

VIII. Q3-SATURATION

The notion of **Q3**-saturation is more complicated than that of **Q1**-saturation. The reason for this is that, in the absence of A7, we must resort to a much more detailed argument to ensure that an analogue of L3 can be proved. First, we define by induction sequences $\mathrm{f}_0, \mathrm{f}_1, \ldots$ and $\mathrm{h}_0, \mathrm{h}_1, \ldots$ of functions. The functions f_n and h_n will be used to guarantee, roughly speaking, that if $\Diamond \cdots \Diamond A \in \boldsymbol{\Gamma}$ (here the $\Diamond$ is repeated n times), then there are saturated sets $\Delta_1, \ldots, \Delta_n$ such that $\boldsymbol{\Gamma} \mathcal{R} \Delta_1$, $\Delta_1 \mathcal{R} \Delta_2, \ldots,$ and $\Delta_{n-1} \mathcal{R} \Delta_n$.

D2. $\mathrm{f}_0((\exists x)A, y) = \Diamond(\exists x)A \supset \Diamond(\mathrm{E}y \wedge A^y/x)$

$\mathrm{f}_1(B, (\exists x)A, y) = \Diamond B \supset \Diamond(B \wedge (\Diamond(\exists x)A \supset \Diamond(\mathrm{E}y \wedge A^y/x)))$

$\mathrm{f}_{i+1}(B_1, \ldots, B_{i+1}, (\exists x)A, y)$

$= \Diamond B_1 \supset \Diamond(B_1 \wedge \mathrm{f}_i(B_2, \ldots, B_{i+1}, (\exists x)A, y))$

D3. $\mathrm{h}_1(B, x, t) = \Diamond B \supset \Diamond(B \wedge x = t)$

$\mathrm{h}_{i+1}(B_1, \ldots, B_{i+1}, x, t) = \Diamond B_1 \supset \Diamond(B_1 \wedge \mathrm{h}_i(B_2, \ldots, B_{i+1}, x, t))$

D4. A subset Γ of $\mathrm{W_M}$ is **Q3**-M-*saturated* (abbreviated '**M**-saturated' below) if it meets the following seven conditions:[9]

(1) Γ is **Q3**-consistent;

(2) For all $A \in \mathrm{W_M}$, $A \in \Gamma$ or $\sim A \in \Gamma$;

(3) For all $A \in \mathrm{W_M}$ and $x \in \mathrm{V_M}$, $(x)A \in \Gamma$ if $A^y/x \in \Gamma$ for all $y \in \mathrm{V_M}$;

(4) For all $t \in T_{\mathrm{M}}$ there is an $x \in \mathrm{V_M}$ such that $x = t \in \Gamma$;

(5) For all $A \in \mathrm{W_M}$ and $x \in \mathrm{V_M}$, there is a $y \in \mathrm{V_M}$ such that $\mathrm{f}_0((\exists x)A, y) \in \Gamma$;

(6) For all $n > 0$, for all $t \in \mathrm{T_M}$ and $\{B_1, \ldots, B_n\} \subseteq \mathrm{W_M}$, there is an $x \in \mathrm{V_M}$ such that $\mathrm{h}_n(B_1, \cdots, B_n, x, t) \in \Gamma$;

(7) For all $n>0$, for all $\{B_1,\ldots, B_n, (\exists x)A\}\subseteq W_M$, there is a $y\in V_M$ such that $f_n(B_1,\ldots, B_n, (\exists x)A, y)\in\Gamma$.

Armed with this definition, we proceed in much the same way as before in proving the semantic completeness of the system. Since, however, many adjustments must be made at various points in the classical argument of Henkin [3], we will furnish more details this time.

L9. For all $n>0$, if $\Gamma\vdash_3 \sim f_n(B_1,\ldots, B_n, (\exists x)A, y)$ and y does not occur free in $B_1,\ldots, B_n, (\exists x)A$, or any member of Γ, then Γ is **Q3**-inconsistent.

PROOF. Induce on n, showing that for all k, if $\Gamma\vdash_3 C_1 \prec .\cdots\prec . C_k \prec \sim f_n(B_1,\ldots, B_n, (\exists x)A, y)$ and y does not occur free in $B_1,\ldots, B_n, (\exists x)A, C_1,\ldots, C_k$, or any member of Γ, then $\Gamma\vdash_3 C_1\prec .\cdots\prec . C_{k-1} \prec\Box\sim C_k$. If $\Gamma\vdash_3 C_1\prec .\cdots\prec . C_k\prec\sim f_1(B, (\exists x)A, y)$, then

$$\text{(i)}\qquad \Gamma\vdash_3 C_1\prec .\cdots\prec . C_k\prec\Diamond B,$$

and

$$\text{(ii)}\qquad \Gamma\vdash_3 C_1\prec .\cdots\prec . C_k\prec . B\prec(\Diamond(\exists x)A\wedge\Box(\mathrm{E}y\supset\sim A^y/x)).$$

From (ii), we see that

$$\text{(iii)}\qquad \Gamma\vdash_3 C_1\prec .\cdots\prec . C_k\prec . B\prec\Diamond(\exists x)A,$$

and

$$\text{(iv)}\qquad \Gamma\vdash_3 C_1\prec .\cdots\prec . C_k\prec . B\prec\Box(\mathrm{E}y\supset\sim A^y/x).$$

Applying R5 to (iv), we have

$$\Gamma\vdash_3 C_1\prec .\cdots\prec . C_k\prec . B\prec\Box(x)(\mathrm{E}x\supset\sim A);$$

hence, by A5′,

$$\text{(v)}\qquad \Gamma\vdash_3 C_1\prec .\cdots\prec C_k\prec . B\prec\Box(x)\sim A.$$

But (iii) and (v) yield $\Gamma\vdash_3 C_1\prec .\cdots\prec . C_k\prec\Box\sim B$, which together with (i) yields what was to be shown, that

$$\Gamma\vdash_3 C_1\prec .\cdots\prec . C_{k-1}\prec\Box\sim C_k$$

(or, in case $k=0$, that Γ is **Q3**-inconsistent).

Suppose now that the property to be established holds for $n=j$. If $\Gamma\vdash_3 C_1\prec .\cdots\prec .\sim f_{j+1}(B_1,\ldots, B_n, (\exists x)A, y)$ then

(vi) $\Gamma \vdash_3 C_1 \prec . \cdots \prec . C_k \prec \Diamond B_1$

and

(vii) $\Gamma \vdash_3 C_1 \prec . \cdots \prec . C_k \prec . B_1 \prec \sim \mathrm{f}_j(B_1, \ldots, B_j, (\exists x) A, y)$.

Applying the hypothesis of induction to (vii), we have

$$\Gamma \vdash_3 C_1 \prec . \cdots \prec . C_k \prec \Box \sim B_1,$$

which together with (vi) yields

$$\Gamma \vdash_3 C_1 \prec . \cdots \prec . C_{k-1} \prec \Box \sim C_k.$$

The lemma, being a special case of the result we have just proved inductively, is now established.

L10. For all $n>0$, if $\Gamma \vdash_3 \sim \mathrm{h}_n(B_1, \ldots, B_n, x, t)$ and x does not occur free in $B_1, \ldots, B_n$, t, or any member of Γ, then Γ is **Q3**-inconsistent.

PROOF: like the proof of L9, but making use of R7 instead of R5.

By a **Q3**-*ω-extension* (abbreviated 'ω-extension' below) of **M**, we understand a morphology **M**′ like **M** except that $\mathrm{V}_{\mathbf{M}'} = \mathrm{V}_{\mathbf{M}} \cup \{z_1, z_2, \ldots\}$, where $z_1, z_2, \ldots$ are symbols foreign to **M**.

L11. Every **Q3**-consistent subset Γ of $\mathrm{W}_{\mathbf{M}}$ has an **M**′-saturated extension $\boldsymbol{\Gamma}$, where **M**′ is any ω-extension of **M**.

PROOF. Let $\mathrm{Z} = \{z_1, z_2, \ldots\}$ be the set of individual variables added to **M** in passing to **M**′. In saturating Γ, we will use a limiting construction in which denumerably many things are done denumerably many times; to index these operations we take a partitioning of the nonnegative integers into denumerably many denumerable sets. $\mathrm{S}_0, \mathrm{S}_1, \mathrm{S}_2, \ldots$. Let Γ_0 be Γ, and define Γ_{i+1} inductively according to the following cases.

(1) $i \in \mathrm{S}_0$. Let $(\exists x)A$ be the alphabetically first formula of **M**′ of the kind $(\exists y)B$ such that for all $z \in \mathrm{Z}$, $((\exists x)A \supset A^z/x) \wedge \mathrm{E}z) \notin \Gamma_i$, and let z be the first member of Z not to occur in any member of Γ_i or in $(\exists x)A$. Then let $\Gamma_{i+1} = \Gamma_i \cup \{((\exists x)A \supset A^z/x) \wedge \mathrm{E}z)\}$.

(2) $i \in \mathrm{S}_1$. Let $(\exists x)A$ be the alphabetically first formula of **M** of the kind $(\exists y)B$ such that for all $z \in \mathrm{Z}$, $\mathrm{f}_0((\exists x)A, z) \notin \Gamma_i$, and let z be the first member of Z not to occur in any member of Γ_i or in $(\exists x)A$. Then let $\Gamma_{i+1} = \Gamma_i \cup \{\mathrm{f}_0((\exists x)A, z)\}$.

(3) $i \in \mathrm{S}_2$. Let t be the alphabetically first term of **M**′ such that for all $z \in \mathrm{Z}$, $z = t \notin \Gamma_i$, and let z be the alphabetically first member of Z not to occur in any member of Γ_i or in t. Then let $\Gamma_{i+1} = \Gamma_i \cup \{z = t\}$.

(4) $i \in S_{2n+1}$, where $n>0$. Let $B_1 \vee \cdots \vee B_n \vee (\exists x)A$ be the alphabetically first formula of $\mathbf{M}'$ of the kind $C_1 \vee \cdots \vee C_n \vee (\exists y)D$ such that for all $z \in Z$, $f_n(B_1, \ldots, B_n, (\exists x)A, z) \notin \Gamma_i$, and let z be the first member of Z not to occur in any member of Γ_i or in $B_1 \vee \cdots \vee B_n \vee (\exists x)A$. Then let $\Gamma_{i+1} = \Gamma_i \cup \{f_n(B_1, \ldots, B_n, (\exists x)A, z)\}$.

(5) $i \in S_{2n+2}$, where $n>0$. Let $B_1 \vee \cdots \vee B_n \vee t=t$ be the alphabetically first formula of $\mathbf{M}'$ of the kind $C_1 \vee \cdots \vee C_n \vee s=s$ such that for all $z \in Z$, $h_n(B_1, \ldots, B_n, z, t) \in \Gamma_i$, and let z be the first member of Z not to occur in any member of Γ_i or in $B_1 \vee \cdots \vee B_n \vee t=t$. Then let $\Gamma_{i+1} = \Gamma_i \cup \{h_n(B_1, \ldots, B_n, z, t)\}$.

We now show by induction that for all i, Γ_i is **Q3**-consistent. In Case 1, if Γ_i were **Q3**-inconsistent we would have

$$\Gamma_i \cup \{((\exists x)A \supset A^z/x) \wedge \mathrm{E}z\} \vdash_3 P \wedge {\sim} P,$$

and hence by T3

$$\Gamma_i \cup \{(\exists x)(((\exists x)A \supset A) \wedge \mathrm{E}x)\} \vdash_3 P \wedge {\sim} P,$$

But then, by T4, we would have

$$\Gamma_i \vdash_3 P \wedge {\sim} P$$

and Γ_i would be **Q3**-inconsistent.

In Case 2, if Γ_{i+1} were **Q3**-inconsistent we would have

(i) $\quad \Gamma_i \vdash_3 \Diamond (\exists x)A$

and

(ii) $\quad \Gamma_i \vdash_3 \Box (\mathrm{E}z \supset {\sim} A^z/x)$.

But then, applying R4 to (ii), we would have

$$\Gamma_i \vdash_3 \Box (x)(\mathrm{E}x \supset {\sim} A),$$

and hence by A5′,

$$\Gamma_i \vdash_3 \Box [(x)] {\sim} A.$$

Putting this together with (i), we see that Γ_i would be **Q3**-inconsistent.

In Case 3, if Γ_{i+1} were **Q3**-inconsistent, we would have $\Gamma_i \vdash_3 {\sim} z=t$ and so, because of R6, Γ_i would be **Q3**-inconsistent.

In Case 4, if Γ_{i+1} were **Q3**-inconsistent, where $i \in S_{2n+1}$ and $n>0$, we would have

$$\Gamma_i \vdash_3 \sim \mathrm{f}_n(B_1, \ldots, B_n, (\exists x)A, z).$$

Applying L9, we see that under these circumstances Γ_i would be **Q3**-inconsistent.

In Case 5, if Γ_{i+1} were **Q3**-inconsistent where $i \in \mathrm{S}_{2n+2}$ and $n > 0$, we would have

$$\Gamma_i \vdash_3 \sim \mathrm{h}_n(B_1, \ldots, B_n, z, t).$$

Applying L10, we see that under these circumstances Γ_i would be **Q3**-inconsistent.

We have now shown that for all i, Γ_i is **Q3**-consistent; therefore $\Delta = \bigcup_{i \in \omega} \Gamma_i$ is **Q3**-consistent. Extending Δ in the usual way to a negation-complete set, we obtain the desired saturated extension of Γ.

Again, we can strengthen L11.

L12. For any $\Gamma \subseteq \mathrm{W}_{\mathbf{M}}$ and ω-extension $\mathbf{M}'$ of $\mathbf{M}$, Γ is **Q3**-consistent iff Γ has an $\mathbf{M}'$-saturated extension $\boldsymbol{\Gamma}$.

Having established analogues for **Q3** of L1 and L2, we turn to the problem of doing the same for L3. With the completion of L13, below, the most difficult part of the completeness proof will be finished.

L13. Let $\boldsymbol{\Gamma}$ be any $\mathbf{M}$-saturated set, let $\Delta_1 \mathscr{R} \Delta_2$ iff $\{A/\Box A \in \Delta_1\} \subseteq \Delta_2$, and let $\mathscr{K}$ be the closure of $\{\boldsymbol{\Gamma}\}$ under $\mathscr{R}$. Then $\mathscr{K}$ satisfies the following condition: for all $\Delta \in \mathscr{K}$ and all $A \in \mathrm{W}_{\mathbf{M}}$, if $\Diamond A \in \Delta$ then there is a $\Delta' \in \mathscr{K}$ such that $A \in \Delta'$ and $\Delta \mathscr{R} \Delta'$.

PROOF.[10] Suppose that $\Delta \in \mathscr{K}$ and that $\Diamond A \in \Delta$. Define by induction a sequence $B_0, B_1, \ldots$ of formulas of $\mathbf{M}$, as follows. Let A be B_0, and as in the proof of L11, above, let $\mathrm{S}_0, \mathrm{S}_1, \ldots$ be a partitioning of the nonnegative integers into denumerably many denumerable sets. Define B_{i+1} by cases in the following way.

(1) If $i \in \mathrm{S}_0$ let C be the alphabetically first formula of $\mathbf{M}$ such that neither $C \in \{B_0, \ldots, B_i\}$ nor $\sim C \in \{B_0, \ldots, B_i\}$. Then let B_{i+1} be C if $\Diamond (B_0 \wedge \cdots \wedge B_i \wedge C) \in \Delta$, and $\sim C$ otherwise,

(2) If $i \in \mathrm{S}_1$ then in case there is no formula of the kind $(\exists y)D \in \{B_0, \ldots, B_i\}$, let B_{i+1} be B_i. And in case there is such a formula, let $(\exists x)C$ be the alphabetically first formula, and let z be the first member of $\mathrm{V}_{\mathbf{M}}$ such that

$$\Diamond (B_0 \wedge \cdots \wedge B_i) \supset \Diamond (B_0 \wedge \cdots \wedge B_i \wedge \mathrm{E}z \wedge C^z/x) \in \Delta.$$

Then let B_{i+1} be $\mathrm{E}z \wedge C^z/x$.

(3) If $i \in S_2$, then let t be the alphabetically first term of M such that $\diamond(B_0 \wedge \cdots \wedge B_i) \supset \diamond(B_0 \wedge \cdots \wedge B_i \wedge z=t) \in \Delta$. Then let B_{i+1} be $z=t$.

(4) If $i \in S_3$, then in case there is no formula of the kind $\diamond(\exists y)D \in \in \{B_0, \ldots, B_i\}$, let B_{i+1} be B_i. And in case there is such a formula, let $(\exists x)C$ be the alphabetically first such formula, and let z be the first member of V_M such that

$$\diamond(B_0 \wedge \cdots \wedge B_i) \supset \diamond(B_0 \wedge \cdots \wedge B_i \wedge f_0((\exists x)C, z)) \in \Delta .$$

Then let B_{i+1} be $Ez \wedge C^z/x$.

(5) If $i \in S_{2n+2}$ (where $n>0$), let $C_1 \vee \cdots \vee C_n \vee t=t$ be the alphabetically first formula of M of the kind $D_1 \vee \cdots \vee D_n \vee s=s$ such that for all $x \in V_M$, $h_n(C_1, \ldots, C_n, x, t) \notin \{B_0, \ldots, B_i\}$, and let z be the alphabetically first member of V_M such that

$$\diamond(B_1 \wedge \cdots \wedge B_i) \supset \diamond(B_1 \wedge \cdots \wedge B_i \wedge h_n(C_1, \ldots, C_n, z, t)) \in \Delta .$$

Then let B_{i+1} be $z=t$.

(6) If $i \in S_{2n+3}$ (where $n>0$), let $C_1 \vee \cdots \vee C_n \vee (\exists x)C$ be the alphabetically first formula of the kind $D_1 \vee \cdots \vee D_n \vee (\exists y)D$ such that for all $x \in V_M$, $f_n(C_1, \ldots, C_n, (\exists x)C, x) \notin \{B_0, \ldots, B_i\}$, and let z be the first member of V_M such that

$$\diamond(B_0 \wedge \cdots \wedge B_i) \supset \diamond(B_0 \wedge \cdots \wedge B_i \wedge f_n(C_1, \ldots, C_n, (\exists x)C, z)) \in \Delta .$$

Then let B_{i+1} be $f_n(C_1, \ldots, C_n, (\exists x)C, z)$.

Now we claim that for all i, B_i is defined and $\diamond(B_0 \wedge \cdots \wedge B_i) \in \Delta$. This is easily shown by induction; our assumption that $\diamond A \in \Delta$ furnishes the basis case. In Case 1 of the construction, it is clear that B_{i+1} is defined, and $\diamond(B_0 \wedge \cdots \wedge B_{i+1}) \in \Delta$ since for all formulas C, if it were the case that $\diamond(B_0 \wedge \cdots \wedge B_i \wedge C) \notin \Delta$ and $\diamond(B_0 \wedge \cdots \wedge B_i \wedge \sim C) \notin \Delta$ then $(B_0 \wedge \cdots \wedge B_i) \prec C \in \Delta$ and $(B_0 \wedge \cdots \wedge B_i) \prec \sim C \in \Delta$ so that we would have $\diamond(B_0 \wedge \cdots \wedge B_i) \notin \Delta$, contrary to assumption.

In Case 2, let u be the alphabetically first variable of M not to occur in any member of $\{B_0, \ldots, B_i\}$, and let $(\exists x)C$ be B_k. Then since $\diamond(B_0 \wedge \cdots \wedge B_i) \in \Delta$, $\diamond(\exists u)$ $(B_0 \wedge \cdots \wedge B_{k-1} \wedge C^u/x \wedge B_{k+1} \wedge \cdots \wedge B_i) \in \Delta$. The M-saturation of Δ guarantees that $\diamond(\exists u)$ $(B_0 \wedge \cdots \wedge B_{k-1} \wedge C^u/x \wedge \wedge B_{k+1} \wedge \cdots \wedge B_i) \supset \diamond(Ez \wedge B_0 \wedge \cdots \wedge B_{k-1} \wedge C^z/x \wedge B_{k+1} \wedge \cdots \wedge B_i) \in \Delta$ for some $z \in V_{\mathbf{M}}$; and hence, since $\vdash_3 (Ez \wedge C^z/x) \supset (\exists x) C$, we have $\Diamond (B_0 \wedge \cdots \wedge B_i \wedge Ez \wedge C^z/x) \in \Delta$; i.e. $\Diamond (B_0 \wedge \cdots \wedge B_{i+1}) \in \Delta$.

In Case 3, B_{i+1} is again defined because the **M**-saturation of Δ guarantees that there is a $z \in V_{\mathbf{M}}$ such that $h_1 (B_0 \wedge \cdots \wedge B_i, z, t) \in \Delta$; in Case 4, B_{i+1} is defined because for some $z \in V_{\mathbf{M}}$, $f_i (B_0, \ldots, B_i, (\exists x) C, z) \in \Delta$. For the same reason, B_{i+1} is defined in Cases 4 and 5, and again the instantiating variable is chosen so that $\Diamond (B_0 \wedge \cdots \wedge B_{i+1}) \in \Delta$ if $\Diamond (B_0 \wedge \wedge \cdots \wedge B_i) \in \Delta$.

Now let $\Delta' = \bigcup_{i \in \omega} B_i$. Clearly, $A \in \Delta'$; we further claim that Δ' is **M**-saturated and that $\Delta \mathcal{R} \Delta'$. The set Δ' is **Q3**-consistent since for every finite subset $\{C_1, \ldots, C_n\}$ of Δ', $\Diamond (C_1 \wedge \cdots \wedge C_n) \in \Delta$ and hence by T5, $\{C_1, \ldots, C_n\}$ is **Q3**-consistent. And Δ' is negation-complete on **M** since Case 1 of the construction ensures that for all C, either $C \in \Delta'$ or $\sim C \in \Delta'$. Similarly, Cases 2, 3, 4, 5, and 6 of the construction guarantee that Δ' fulfills clauses 3, 4, 5, 6, and 7, respectively, of D4. Thus, Δ' is **M**-saturated.

Furthermore, suppose that $\Box C \in \Delta$; then $C \in \Delta'$, since if $\sim C \in \Delta'$ then we would have $\Diamond \sim C \in \Delta$, contrary to assumption. Therefore $\Delta \mathcal{R} \Delta'$.

This completes the proof of L13.

IX. SEMANTICS OF Q3

A **Q3-S4**-*model structure* (in the present paper, abbreviated '**Q3**ms') is a quadruple $\langle \mathcal{K}, \mathcal{R}, \mathcal{D}, \mathcal{D}' \rangle$, where $\mathcal{K}$ is a nonempty set, $\mathcal{R}$ a binary reflexive and transitive relation on $\mathcal{K}$, $\mathcal{D}$ a function taking members α of $\mathcal{K}$ into nonempty domains $\mathcal{D}_\alpha$, and $\mathcal{D}'$ a set disjoint with $\bigcup_{\alpha \in \mathcal{K}} \mathcal{D}_\alpha$, such that for all $\beta \in \mathcal{K}$, $(\mathcal{D}' \cup \bigcup_{\alpha \in \mathcal{K}} \mathcal{D}_\alpha) - \mathcal{D}_\beta$ is nonempty.

Let $\mathcal{D} = \mathcal{D}' \cup \bigcup_{\alpha \in \mathcal{K}} \mathcal{D}_\alpha$ be the set of all individuals associated with the **Q3**ms $\langle \mathcal{K}, \mathcal{R}, \mathcal{D}, \mathcal{D}' \rangle$. A **Q3**-*interpretation* I of a morphology **M** on a **Q3**ms $\langle \mathcal{K}, \mathcal{R}, \mathcal{D}, \mathcal{D}' \rangle$ is a function which, for each $\alpha \in \mathcal{K}$, assigns:

(1) To each $x \in V_{\mathbf{M}}$ a member $I(x)$ of $\mathcal{D}$;

(2) To each $c \in C_{\mathbf{M}}$ a member $I_\alpha (c)$ of $\mathcal{D}$;

(3) To each $P^0 \in P^0_{\mathbf{M}}$ a value $I_\alpha (P^0)$ in $\{T, F\}$ and to each $P^i \in P^i_{\mathbf{M}} (i > 0)$ a subset $I_\alpha (P^i)$ of the cartesian product $\mathcal{D}^i$.

Again, where $d \in \mathcal{D}$, I^d/x is the interpretation differing (if at all) from I only in assigning d to x.

The truth-value $I_\alpha (A)$ in α of a formula A under a **Q3**-interpretation I on a **Q3**ms $\langle \mathcal{K}, \mathcal{R}, \mathcal{D}, \mathcal{D}' \rangle$, and the value $I_\alpha (t)$ assigned in α to a term t

under such an interpretation, are defined by simultaneous induction. This time we omit the clauses for sentential connectives, which are exactly like the corresponding clauses in the case of **Q1**. First, let $I_\alpha(x) = I(x)$, for all $\alpha \in \mathscr{K}$.

(1) $I_\alpha(Pt_1 \ldots t_n) = T$ if $\langle I_\alpha(t_1), \ldots, I_\alpha(t_n) \rangle \in I_\alpha(P)$,
$I_\alpha(Pt_1 \ldots t_n) = F$ otherwise;

(2) $I_\alpha(\imath_k A) =$ the unique $d \in \mathscr{D}_\alpha$ such that $I^d/x_\alpha(A) = T$, if there is such an individual d, $I_\alpha(\imath_x A) =$ an arbitrary[11] member of $\mathscr{D}' - \mathscr{D}_\alpha$ otherwise;[12]

(3) $I_\alpha(s=t) = T$ if $I_\alpha(s) = I_\alpha(t)$,
$I_\alpha(s=t) = F$ otherwise;

(7) $I_\alpha((x)A) = T$ if for all $d \in \mathscr{D}_\alpha$, $I^d/x_\alpha(A) = T$,
$I_\alpha((x)A) = F$ otherwise.

Again, we record for later use a lemma concerning substitution.

L14. Let I be an interpretation of **M** on a **Q3**ms $\langle \mathscr{K}, \mathscr{R}, \mathscr{D}, \mathscr{D}' \rangle$ and let $I(y) = d$, where $y \in V_{\mathbf{M}}$. Then $I^d/x_\alpha(A) = I_\alpha(A^y/x)$.

The notions of *simultaneous* **Q3**-*satisfiability* and of **Q3**-*validity* are defined as in the case of **Q1**.

L15. Let I be an interpretation of **M** on a **Q3**ms $\langle \mathscr{K}, \mathscr{R}, \mathscr{D}, \mathscr{D}' \rangle$ such that for all $d \in \mathscr{D}$ there is an $x \in V_{\mathbf{M}}$ such that $I(x) = d$. Let $\alpha \in \mathscr{K}$. Then the set $\Gamma = \{A / I_\alpha(A) = T \text{ and } A \in W_{\mathbf{M}}\}$ of formulas of **M** simultaneously **Q3**-satisfied by I in α is **M**-saturated.

PROOF. Again, we can easily check that the axioms of **Q3** are all **Q3**-valid and that **Q3**-validity is preserved by the rules of proof of **Q3**. Condition (1), as before, follows immediately from this, and condition (2) is trivial. To establish condition (3), suppose that $(x)A \in \Gamma$; then for some $d \in \mathscr{D}_\alpha$, $I^d/x_\alpha(A) = F$. Let $I(y) = d$; by L13, $I_\alpha(A^y/x) = F$, and y has been chosen so that $Ey \in \Gamma$. Conditions (4)–(7) are verified in the same way.

X. SEMANTIC COMPLETENESS OF Q3

L16. Let Γ be **M**-saturated. Then there is an interpretation I of **M** on a **Q3**ms $\langle \mathscr{K}, \mathscr{R}, \mathscr{D}, \mathscr{D}' \rangle$ and an $\alpha \in \mathscr{K}$ such that Γ is the set of formulas of **M** simultaneously **Q3**-satisfied by I in α.

PROOF. Let $\mathscr{R}$ be as in L13, and let $\mathscr{K}$ be the closure of $\{\Gamma\}$ under $\mathscr{R}$. The relation $\simeq$ on $V_{\mathbf{M}}$ such that $x \simeq y$ iff $x = y \in \Gamma$ is an equivalence relation and hence divides $V_{\mathbf{M}}$ into disjoint partitions; let $\mathscr{D}^*$ be a set of representatives, one from each of these partitions, and let $\mathrm{f}(x)$ be the representative of the partition to which x belongs. Define a function $\mathscr{D}$ from $\mathscr{K}$ into subsets of $\mathscr{D}^*$, as follows: $\mathscr{D}_\Delta = \{\mathrm{f}(x)/x \in \mathrm{V_M}$ and $\mathrm{E}x \in \Delta\}$. Since $\vdash_3 (\exists x)\,\mathrm{E}x$, $\mathscr{D}_\Delta$ is nonempty for all $\Delta \in \mathscr{K}$. Finally, let $\mathscr{D}' = \{\mathrm{f}(x)/x \in \mathrm{V_M}$ and for all $\Delta \in \mathscr{K}$, $\sim \mathrm{E}x \in \Delta\}$. It is easily verified that $\mathscr{D}' = \mathscr{D}^* - \bigcup_{\Delta \in \mathscr{K}} \mathscr{D}_\Delta$. Also, for all $\Delta \in \mathscr{K}$, $\mathscr{D}^* - \mathscr{D}_\Delta$ is nonempty, for because Δ is **M**-saturated there is a $y \in \mathrm{V_M}$ such that $y = \imath_x (P \wedge \sim P) \in \Delta$; but $\mathrm{f}(y) \in \mathscr{D}^*$ and $\mathrm{f}(y) \notin \mathscr{D}_\Delta$.

A2 and A3 again ensure that $\mathscr{R}$ is reflexive and transitive; it follows that the quadruple $\langle \mathscr{K}, \mathscr{R}, \mathscr{D}, \mathscr{D}' \rangle$ is a Q3ms. We now define an interpretation I of **M** on $\langle \mathscr{K}, \mathscr{R}, \mathscr{D}, \mathscr{D}' \rangle$.

For all $t \in \mathrm{T_M}$ and all $\Delta \in \mathscr{K}$, there is an $x \in \mathrm{V_M}$ such that $x = t \in \Delta$; let $\mathrm{g}_\Delta(t)$ be $\mathrm{f}(x)$. (The value $\mathrm{g}_\Delta(t)$ is independent of the choice of x, since if $x = t \in \Delta$ and $y = t \in \Delta$, then $x = y \in \Delta$ and hence $\Diamond x = y \in \Gamma$; therefore $x = y \in \Gamma$ and $\mathrm{f}(x) = \mathrm{f}(y)$.) Notice that for all $x \in \mathrm{V_M}$ and $\Delta \in \mathscr{K}$, $\mathrm{f}(x) = \mathrm{g}_\Delta(x)$.

For all $x \in \mathrm{V_M}$, let $\mathrm{I}(x) = \mathrm{f}(x)$; for all $c \in \mathrm{C_M}$, let $\mathrm{I}_\Delta(c) = \mathrm{g}_\Delta(c)$; for all $P^0 \in \mathrm{P^0_M}$, let $\mathrm{I}_\Delta(P^0) = \mathrm{T}$ if $P^0 \in \Delta$ and $\mathrm{I}_\Delta(P^0) = \mathrm{F}$ if $P^0 \notin \Delta$; and where $i > 0$, for all $P^i \in \mathrm{P^i_M}$ let $\mathrm{I}_\Delta(P^i) = \{\langle \mathrm{f}(x_1), \ldots, \mathrm{f}(x_i)\rangle / \mathrm{P}^i x_1 \ldots x_i \in \Delta\}$. In case there is no unique $\mathrm{d} \in \mathscr{D}_\Delta$ such that $\mathrm{I^d}/x_\Delta(A) = \mathrm{T}$, let $\mathrm{I}_\Delta(\imath_x A)$ be $\mathrm{g}_\Delta(\imath_x A)$. To ensure that I, thus defined, is an interpretation of **M** on $\langle \mathscr{K}, \mathscr{R}, \mathscr{D}, \mathscr{D}' \rangle$ we must show that under these circumstances $\mathrm{g}_\Delta(\imath_x A) \in \mathscr{D}_\Delta$. This will follow from the argument below.

By simultaneous induction on the complexity of A and t, we show that for all $A \in \mathrm{W_M}$, $t \in \mathrm{T_M}$, and $\Delta \in \mathscr{K}$, $\mathrm{I}_\Delta(A) = \mathrm{T}$ iff $A \in \Delta$, and that $\mathrm{I}_\Delta(t) = \mathrm{g}_\Delta(t)$. We will omit the Cases (6, 7, and 8) of the induction concerning sentential connectives; the remaining cases are as follows.

CASE 1. A is $P^i t_1 \ldots t_i$. By the definition of satisfaction, $\mathrm{I}_\Delta(P^i t_1 \ldots t_i) = \mathrm{T}$ iff $\langle \mathrm{I}_\Delta(t_1), \ldots, \mathrm{I}_\Delta(t_i)\rangle \in \mathrm{I}_\Delta(P^i)$. By the hypothesis of induction, $\mathrm{I}_\Delta(t_k) = \mathrm{g}_\Delta(t_k)$, for $1 \leqslant k \leqslant i$; hence, $\langle \mathrm{I}_\Delta(t_1), \ldots, \mathrm{I}_\Delta(t_i)\rangle \in \mathrm{I}_\Delta(P^i)$ iff $\langle \mathrm{g}_\Delta(t_1), \ldots, \mathrm{g}_\Delta(t_i)\rangle \in \mathrm{I}_\Delta(P^i)$. Now, for all k, $1 \leqslant k < i$, there is an $x_k \in \mathrm{V_M}$ such that $x_k = t_k \in \Delta$ and $\mathrm{f}(x_k) = \mathrm{g}_\Delta(t_k)$; therefore $\langle \mathrm{g}_\Delta(t_1), \ldots, \mathrm{g}_\Delta(t_i)\rangle \in \mathrm{I}_\Delta(P^i)$ iff $\langle \mathrm{f}(x_1), \ldots, \mathrm{f}(x_i)\rangle \in \mathrm{I}_\Delta(P^i)$. But by the definition of I, $\langle \mathrm{f}(x_1), \ldots, \mathrm{f}(x_i)\rangle \in \mathrm{I}_\Delta(P^i)$ iff $P^i x_1 \ldots x_n \in \Delta$, and in view of A8′, $P^i x_1 \ldots x_n \in \Delta$ iff $P^i t_1 \ldots t_i \in \Delta$.

CASE 2. The term t is x where $x \in \mathrm{V_M}$. By definition, $\mathrm{I}_\Delta(t) = \mathrm{f}(x) = \mathrm{g}_\Delta(x)$.

CASE 3. The term t is c, where $c \in \mathrm{C_M}$. By definition, $\mathrm{I}_\Delta(c) = \mathrm{g}_\Delta(c)$.

CASE 4. A is $s=t$. By the hypothesis of induction, $I_\Delta(t)=g_\Delta(t)$ and $I_\Delta(s)=g_\Delta(s)$. By the definition of satisfaction, $I_\Delta(s=t)=T$ iff $I_\Delta(s)=I_\Delta(t)$, and this holds iff $g_\Delta(s)=g_\Delta(t)$. But this holds iff there is an $x\in V_M$ such that $x=s\in\Delta$ and $x=t\in\Delta$, and (again, using A8′), this holds iff $s=t\in\Delta$.

CASE 5. The term t is $\iota_x B$. Suppose first that there is no unique $d\in\mathscr{D}_\Delta$ such that $I^d/x_\Delta(B)=T$. Then by definition, $I_\Delta(t)=g_\Delta(t)$. On the other hand, suppose that there exists a unique $f(y)\in\mathscr{D}_\Delta$ such that $I^{f(y)}/x_\Delta(B)=T$. Using properties of M-saturation, it is easy to see that in this case, $(x)(B\equiv x=f(y))\in\Delta$. But then, in view of A10′ and A4′, we have $E\Box f(y)\supset f(y)=\iota_x B\in\Delta$; and by T6, $E\Box f(y)\in\Delta$ since $Ef(y)\in\Delta$, so that $f(y)=\iota_x B\in\Delta$. Therefore, $g_\Delta(\iota_x B)=f(y)$. But, by the definition of satisfaction, $I_\Delta(\iota_x B)=f(y)$.

CASE 9. A is $(x)B$. By condition (3) of D3, $A\in\Delta$ iff for all $y\in V_M$ such that $Ey\in\Delta$, $B^y/x\in\Delta$. By T7, this holds iff for all $y\in\mathscr{D}_\Delta$, $B^y/x\in\Delta$; and by the hypothesis of induction, this in turn holds iff for all $y\in\mathscr{D}_\Delta$, $I_\Delta(B^y/x)=$ $=T$. By L14, this is equivalent to the condition that for all $y\in\mathscr{D}_\Delta$, $I^y/x_\Delta(B)=T$; and by the definition of satisfaction, this iff $I_\Delta(B)=T$.

Now that this property of I has been established by induction, we can return to the problem of showing I to be an interpretation. Suppose that there is no unique $d\in\mathscr{D}_\Delta$ such that $I^d/x_\Delta(A)=T$. Then, clearly, $(\exists!x)A\notin\Delta$, and so, by A9′, $E\iota_x A\notin\Delta$. But then by A8′, $E(g_\Delta(\iota_x A))\notin\Delta$ and hence $I_\Delta(\iota_x A)\notin\mathscr{D}_\Delta$. Thus, I is an interpretation of **M** on $\langle\mathscr{K},\mathscr{R},\mathscr{D},\mathscr{D}'\rangle$.

The induction above establishes that $\Gamma=\{A/I_\Gamma(A)=T\}$, and so L16 is proved.

The following lemmas and theorems are proved in the same way as L7, L8, T1, and T2, above.

L17. A set Γ is **M**-saturated iff for some **Q3**ms $\langle\mathscr{K},\mathscr{R},\mathscr{D},\mathscr{D}'\rangle$ and interpretation I of **M** on $\langle\mathscr{K},\mathscr{R},\mathscr{D},\mathscr{D}'\rangle$ such that for all $d\in\mathscr{D}^*$ there is an $x\in V_M$ such that $I(x)=d$, there exists an $\alpha\in\mathscr{K}$ such that $\Gamma=$ $=\{A/I_\alpha(A)=T\}$.

L18. Let **M**′ be an ω-extension of **M**, and Γ a subset of W_M. Then Γ is simultaneously **Q3**-satisfiable iff Γ has an **M**′-saturated extension Γ.

T3. (Strong semantic completeness of **Q3**).[13] A subset Γ of W_M is **Q3**-consistent iff Γ is simultaneously **Q3**-satisfiable.

T4. For all formulas A, A is **Q3**-valid iff $\vdash_3 A$.

With these theorems, the main theme of this paper is completed. We conclude with a brief account of how T3 may be used to demonstrate the semantic completeness of yet another system of modal predicate calculus.

XI. THE SYSTEM $\mathbf{Q3^p}$

This system is a deductive extension of **Q3**; it is obtained by adding an axiom of permanence, $(x)\Box Ex$, to the axioms and rules of **Q3**. Intuitively, the meaning of this axiom is that no individual ever passes out of existence. The system $\mathbf{Q3^p}$ is closely related to the system of modal predicate calculus of Hintikka [5], chapter 6.

A $\mathbf{Q3^p}$ms can be defined by adding to the definition of a **Q3**ms $\langle \mathscr{K}, \mathscr{R}, \mathscr{D}, \mathscr{D}' \rangle$ the requirement that for all α, $\beta \in \mathscr{K}$, $\mathscr{D}_\alpha \subseteq \mathscr{D}_\beta$. In the usual way, this yields corresponding notions of simultaneous $\mathbf{Q3^p}$-satisfiability and of $\mathbf{Q3^p}$-validity.

T5. (Strong semantic completeness of $\mathbf{Q3^p}$). A subset Γ of W_M is $\mathbf{Q3^p}$-consistent iff Γ is simultaneously $\mathbf{Q3^p}$-satisfiable.

Proof. Γ is $\mathbf{Q3^p}$-consistent iff $\Gamma \cup \{(x)\Box Ex\}$ is **Q3**-consistent. By T3, $\Gamma \cup \{(x)\Box Ex\}$ is **Q3**-consistent iff $\Gamma \cup \{(x)\Box Ex\}$ is simultaneously **Q3**-satisfiable. Let $\langle \mathscr{K}, \mathscr{R}, \mathscr{D}, \mathscr{D}' \rangle$ be a **Q3**ms, and I an interpretation of **M** on $\langle \mathscr{K}, \mathscr{R}, \mathscr{D}, \mathscr{D}' \rangle$ such that for some $\alpha \in \mathscr{K}$, $I_\alpha((x)\Box Ex) = T$. Let $\mathscr{K}^*$ be the closure of $\{\alpha\}$ under $\mathscr{R}$; clearly, $\langle \mathscr{K}^*, \mathscr{R}, \mathscr{D}, \mathscr{D}' \rangle$ is a $\mathbf{Q3^p}$ms, and $I'_\alpha(A) = T$ iff $I_\alpha(A) = T$, where I′ is the restriction of I to $\langle \mathscr{K}^*, \mathscr{R}, \mathscr{D}, \mathscr{D}' \rangle$. Therefore, if $\Gamma \cup \{(x)\Box Ex\}$ is simultaneously $\mathbf{Q3^p}$-satisfiable then Γ is $\mathbf{Q3^p}$-satisfiable. On the other hand, since every $\mathbf{Q3^p}$ms is a **Q3**ms, if Γ is $\mathbf{Q3^p}$-satisfiable then $\Gamma \cup \{(x)\Box Ex\}$ is **Q3**-satisfiable. Therefore, Γ is $\mathbf{Q3^p}$-consistent iff Γ is simultaneously $\mathbf{Q3^p}$-satisfiable.

As usual, we obtain as a corollary the weak semantic completeness of $\mathbf{Q3^p}$.

T6. For all formulas A of **M**, A is $\mathbf{Q3^p}$-valid iff A is a theorem of $\mathbf{Q3^p}$.

Yale University

BIBLIOGRAPHY

[1] Church, A., *Introduction to Mathematical Logic*, vol. I, Princeton 1956.
[2] Cocchiarella, N., *Tense Logic: a Study of Temporal Reference*. Dissertation, The University of California, Los Angeles, 1966.
[3] Henkin, L., 'The Completeness of the First-Order Functional Calculus', *Journal of Symbolic Logic* **14** (1949) 159–166.
[4] Henkin, L., 'A Generalization of the Concept of ω-Completeness', *Journal of Symbolic Logic* **22** (1957) 1–14.

[5] Hintikka, J., *Knowledge and Belief.* Ithaca, New York, 1962.
[6] Kripke, S., 'A Completeness Theorem in Modal Logic', *Journal of Symbolic Logic* **24** (1959) 1–14.
[7] Kripke, S., 'Semantical Analysis of Modal Logic I: Normal Propositional Calculi', *Zeitschrift für Mathematische Logik und Grundlagen der Mathematik* **9** (1963) 67–96.
[8] Kripke, S., 'Semantical Considerations on Modal and Intuitionistic Logic I' in *Proceedings of a Colloquium on Modal and Many-Valued Logics*, Helsinki 1963, pp. 83–94.
[9] Kripke, S., 'Semantical Analysis of Intuitionistic Logic I' in *Formal Systems and Recursive Functions* (ed. by J. Crossley and M. Dummett), Amsterdam 1965, pp. 92–130.
[10] Montague, R. and L. Henkin, 'On the Definition of "Formal Deduction"', *Journal of Symbolic Logic* **21** (1957) 129–136.
[11] Stalnaker, R. and R. Thomason, 'Abstraction in First-Order Modal Logic', *Theoria* (Lund), **14** (1968) 203–207.
[12] Thomason, R., 'On the Strong Semantical Completeness of the Intuitionistic Predicate Calculus', *Journal of Symbolic Logic* **33** (1968) 1–7.
[13] Thomason, R., 'Modal Logic and Metaphysics' in *The Logical Way of Doing Things* (ed. by K. Lambert), New Haven, Conn., 1969, pp. 119–146.
[14] van Fraassen, B. and K. Lambert, 'On Free Description Theory', *Zeitschrift für Mathematische Logik und Grundlagen der Mathematik* **13** (1967) 225–240.

REFERENCES

* The research leading to this paper was supported under National Science Foundation grant GS-1567. I am indebted to Professor Nino Cocchiarella for comments on an earlier draft of this paper.

[1] The system **Q2** is discussed in Thomason [13], where a definition of **Q2**-validity is given. Prof. David Kaplan has informed me (in a private communication, April, 1967) that the notion of **Q2**-validity cannot be recursively axiomatized.

[2] The system **Q3** is a generalization of the version of modal predicate calculus described in Kripke [8], which treats only closed formulas, and hence gives no account of individual constants or definite descriptions. On the other hand, the system **Q1S5** of modal predicate calculus based on an **S5**-type modality and on a **Q1**-type theory of quantification and identity is the system proved semantically complete in Kripke [6]. In this case our generalization of Kripke's results consists in allowing for sorts of modality other than **S5**, and in proving strong rather than weak completeness.

[3] We will use dots in the usual way in place of parentheses; see Church [1], pp. 74–80.

[4] This proof requires that the morphology (i.e. the set of formulas of the morphology) be denumerable.

[5] See the articles of Kripke, especially [7] and [8], for an intuitive account of this semantics. Another discussion of this sort may be found in Thomason [13].

[6] The requirement that the domains be nonempty is easily lifted; in this case, one must also drop A6′ from the system **Q3**.

[7] This is the only place in the proof of semantic completeness which must be changed to adjust the argument to kinds of modality other than **S4**.

[8] The rules R4–R7 are needed for the proof of semantic completeness of **Q3**. At present, it is not known whether these rules are redundant.

[9] We will use individual variables for instantiation rather than individual constants, as is usual in versions of Henkin's proof and as we ourselves have done in the case of **Q1**. The underlying reason for this is semantic; in **Q3**, individual constants and individual variables are wholly different. Whereas variables range over things (i.e. things-as-identified-across worlds), constants need not be assigned one thing; they may name different things in different worlds.

[10] The proof we give of this lemma makes use of our assumption that the morphology is denumerable.

[11] This can be made more precise by adding to the definition of a **Q3**-interpretation on $\langle \mathscr{K}, \mathscr{R}, \mathscr{D}, \mathscr{D}' \rangle$ an auxiliary function which selects for each definite description $\imath_x A$ and member α of $\mathscr{K}$ an element of $\mathscr{D} - \mathscr{D}_\alpha$ to be assigned to $\imath_x A$ in case the unique-existence condition fails.

[12] Our account of descriptions differs only in minor respects from the theory given in van Fraassen and Lambert [14] of the system **FD**.

[13] A version of T4 is established in Cocchiarella [2] by means of semantic tableaux, for a system of modal predicate calculus with tense-operators. When a connective corresponding to necessity is defined in terms of these operators a system equivalent to our **Q3** is obtained. Cocchiarella later proved a compactness theorem for his system, which together with his weak completeness theorem yields a result implying our T3. This, however, has not yet appeared in print.

The results appearing in the present paper are, to my knowledge, the first Henkin-style completeness proofs for systems such as **Q3**. As I see it, the principal advantage of these results is their flexibility. They are very easy to adapt to other systems, especially to ones obtained by extending the language of **Q3**. For an example of such an application, see Stalnaker and Thomason [11].

H. LEBLANC AND R. K. MEYER

TRUTH-VALUE SEMANTICS FOR THE THEORY OF TYPES

1. Gödel showed in 1931 that the valid wffs of *T*, the simple theory of types, outrun the theorems of *T*, and in fact cannot but outrun them. It was to be almost two decades before Henkin supplied a semantic characterization of these theorems, when he showed in [5] that a wff *A* of *T* is provable in *T* if and only if *A* is what he called *valid in the general sense* or what we shall call *generally valid.* Further semantic characterizations of provability in *T* then came in rapid succession, among them Hintikka [7] and Schütte [12]. Both of these dispense with Henkin's general models, the former using general model sets, the latter total valuations.

Pursuing earlier investigations of Leblanc into first-order and second-order implication,[1] we submit a semantic characterization of derivability (and hence provability) in *T*, and show that a wff *A* of *T* is derivable in *T* from a set $\mathfrak{S}$ of wffs if and only if *A* is what we call *generally implied by* $\mathfrak{S}$. Our account of general implication is an extension of Schütte's account of general validity, our *general truth-value functions* coinciding in effect with his total valuations; accordingly our account also dispenses with general models, though we shall show how the account presented here is foreshadowed in the Henkin techniques. We then go on to offer an account of implication (and hence validity) in *T*, in which what we call *truth-value functions* do duty for models of the ordinary sort. Our results, easily extended to the whole functional calculus of order ω, may be of interest to readers of a nominalist persuasion. Thanks are due to Hintikka, who helped to devise the account of first-order implication in [8] and, by extension, the present account of general implication in *T*.

I

2. We shall take *the primitive signs* of *T* to be the two connectives '$\sim$' and '$\supset$', the membership predicate '$\in$', the colon ':', the two parentheses '(' and ')', and the two braces '{' and '}', and for each natural number

K. Lambert (ed.), Philosophical Problems in Logic.

t from 0 on $\aleph_0$ variables and $\aleph_0$ parameters of type t.[2] We shall understand by *a formula of T* any finite sequence of primitive signs of T, and we shall presume that the formulas of T (in particular, the ones we care about, soon to receive the honorific 'well-formed') have been arranged in sequence, and hence have an *alphabetical order*. We shall refer to the variables of T by means of 'X', 'Y', and 'Z'; to the parameters of T by means of 'P', 'Q', and 'R'; to the formulas of T by means of 'S'. These letters (and others adopted later for similar purposes) will occasionally sport primes or numerical subscripts. We shall take an occurrence of X in S to be *bound* if it is in a part of S of the sort $(X)S'$ or $\{X:S'\}$ and otherwise to be *free*. We shall say that *X occurs bound (free) in S* if at least one occurrence of X in S is bound (free). Finally, we shall take $S(S'/X)$ to be the result of substituting S' for every *free* occurrence of X in S; $S(S'/P)$, to be the result of substituting S' for every occurrence of P in S.

The *well-formed formulas of T* shall be its *terms* and *sentences*, to be immediately defined. We shall refer to the terms of T by 'K', 'L', and 'M', and to the sentences by 'A', 'B', and 'C'. Letting t be any type from 0 on, we proceed to the appropriate recursive definitions.

(i) Let X be a variable and P be a parameter of the same type t. Then $\{X:A(X/P)\}$ is an *abstract* of type $t+1$.

(ii) If S is a parameter or abstract (of type t), S is a term (of type t).

(iii) If K is of type t and L is of type $t+1$, $K \in L$ is a sentence.

(iv) $\sim A$ and $(A \supset B)$ are sentences.

(v) Let X and P be as in (i). Then $(X)A(X/P)$ is a sentence.

A formula S shall be well formed only if (possibly iterated) application of (i)–(v) establishes that it is a term or a sentence. (In view of what seems to have become current practice, however, we shall restrict our application of the abbreviation 'wff' to those well-formed formulas which are sentences.) Although the reader will have noted that officially formulas with free variables are not well formed, we slacken our conventions to the extent of occasionally referring to *sentences* by '$(X)A$' and '$A(K/X)$', and to *terms* by '$\{X:A\}$', etc., when A is $B(X/P)$ for some sentence B. And note finally that if $(X)S$ is a wff, where X is free in S, $S(K/X)$ is a wff only if K and X are of the same type.

We name now certain sets of well-formed formulas. Π shall be the set of all parameters of T; λ, the set of all terms of T; for a given type t, Π_t and λ_t shall be respectively the sets of all parameters and of all terms of that type. In view of the parenthetical remark of the last paragraph, W shall be the set of sentences of T. Finally, '$\mathfrak{S}$', subscripted, primed, or otherwise defaced, shall refer to an arbitrary subset of W.

Our last terminological preliminaries will set the stage for the Hintikka-Leblanc ploy exploited in [8]. Since moralistically inclined readers may, when they discover what is going on, accuse us of undue gimmickry, we advise them to skip this paragraph, continuing for the benefit of the more devious among you. As readers of [4] will recall, in proving that every consistent set $\mathfrak{S}$ of first-order formulas has a model, Henkin was obliged to send out in mid-proof for a fresh supply of constants foreign to $\mathfrak{S}$. The reason, essentially, is that a constant (or parameter) which occurs in $\mathfrak{S}$ is subject therein to special assumptions, while Henkin required for his purposes constants about which no special assumptions were made. Since in the extreme case every constant of a given language might occur in a given set of consistent sentences, it would seem that for the purpose of proving completeness we cannot make do, in general, with the linguistic resources already at hand.

In fact this is false; indeed, Henkin himself avoids the problem in [5] by making use of a choice operator, as he notes. Even without such an operator, however, the problem may be skirted by systematically *re-writing* the formulas of a given $\mathfrak{S}$ in such a way that, when the re-writing is complete, infinitely many parameters do not occur in the set $\mathfrak{S}'$ of re-written formulas. This is essentially the method of [8], and it serves to motivate the definitions immediately following; the point is that we do not need to exceed the vocabulary of T, so far as our formal language is concerned, in deriving our most interesting results about T.

As we proceed, the key notion at which we are aiming is that of the isomorphism of two sets $\mathfrak{S}$ and $\mathfrak{S}'$ of wffs. First, let us call any function f partially defined on the set λ of terms of T with values in λ *type-preserving* provided that, for each type t and each term K of λ_t on which f is defined, $f(K)$ is also in λ_t. Let f be a type-preserving function defined for each parameter P of a given wff A; by the *f-image* of A we mean the result of simultaneously replacing P with $f(P)$ throughout A, for every P in A.[3] Then we say that two sets $\mathfrak{S}$ and $\mathfrak{S}'$ of wffs are *isomorphic* provided that, where $\Pi(\mathfrak{S})$ is the set of all parameters occurring in wffs of $\mathfrak{S}$, there is a one-one type-preserving mapping $f: \Pi(\mathfrak{S}) \rightarrow \Pi$ such that $\mathfrak{S}'$ consists of exactly the f-images of members of $\mathfrak{S}$.[4] In terms of our motivating remarks, two sets are isomorphic iff each can be obtained from the other by a systematic re-writing of parameters.

We say now that a sign of T is *foreign to A* if it does not occur in A, and *foreign to* $\mathfrak{S}$ if it is foreign to every member of $\mathfrak{S}$. We call $\mathfrak{S}$ *infinitely extendible* if, for each t from 0 on, $\aleph_0$ parameters of Π_t are foreign to $\mathfrak{S}$. We pause for a trivial lemma.

LEMMA 1. Every set $\mathfrak{S}$ of sentences of T is isomorphic to an infinitely extendible set.

PROOF. Let P_i^t be the ith parameter in alphabetical order of Π_t, and define $f:\Pi\to\Pi$ by $f(P_i^t)=P_{2i}^t$, for all i and t. Clearly an f-image exists for each $A\in W$, where W is the set of *all* sentences of T, but infinitely many parameters of every type (specifically, all parameters P_{2i+1}^t, $0\leqslant i, t$) fail to occur among the f-images. Accordingly, for any $\mathfrak{S}\subseteq W$ the set $\mathfrak{S}'$ of f-images of members of $\mathfrak{S}$ is infinitely extendible, while it follows readily from definitions that $\mathfrak{S}$ and $\mathfrak{S}'$ are isomorphic.

3. Our last immediate syntactical concern will be provability in T. We shall count as *an axiom of T* any wff of T of the following ten sorts:[5]

A1. $A\supset(B\supset A)$

A2. $(A\supset(B\supset C))\supset((A\supset B)\supset(A\supset C))$

A3. $(\sim A\supset\sim B)\supset(B\supset A)$

A4. $(X)(A\supset B)\supset((X)A\supset(X)B)$

A5. $A\supset(X)A$

A6. $(X)A\supset A(P/X)$

A7. $(X)A\supset A(\{Y:B\}/X)$[6]

A8. $K\in\{X:A\}\equiv A(K/X)$[7]

A9. $(X)(X\in K\equiv X\in L)\supset(K\in M\supset L\in M)$[8]

A10. $(X)A(X/P)$, where A is an axiom and P is foreign to any part of A of the sort $(X)B$ or $\{X:B\}$.[9]

We shall count as *a derivation of A from* $\mathfrak{S}$ *in T (a proof of A in T* when $\mathfrak{S}$ is $\emptyset$, for short) any column of wffs of T that closes with A and every one of whose entries belongs to $\mathfrak{S}$, is an axiom of T, or follows from two previous entries in the column by *Modus Ponens*. And we say that (i) A is *derivable from* $\mathfrak{S}$ *in T* ($\mathfrak{S}\vdash A$, for short) if there is a derivation of A from $\mathfrak{S}$ in T, and (ii) A is *provable in T* ($\vdash A$, for short) if there is a proof of A in T. Finally, (iii) $\mathfrak{S}$ is *consistent in T* if it is not the case that $\mathfrak{S}\vdash\sim(A\supset A)$, for any A.

A few remarks concerning the above axiom system for T may be in order.

(1) In A8 'P' could replace 'K', and in A9 'P', 'Q', and 'R' could replace 'K', 'L', and 'M', respectively. However, the axioms of T are more easily shown to be generally valid when A8 and A9 are written out as above.

(2) Readers who prefer to dispense with set abstracts and the accompanying notation (defining $P \in \{X:A\}$ and $\{X:A\} \in K$ as we did in reference 6) may dispense with A8 above and with condition (v) in the definition of a general truth-value function for T in Section 4 below. A8 corresponds to one of Quine's definitions of $P \in \{X:A\}$ in [11]. While axiom-chopping, we discovered the following proof in T of the biconditional corresponding to Quine's definition of $\{X:A\} \in K$.[10]

(1) $\{X:A\} \in K \supset ((Z)(Z \in \{X:A\} \equiv Z \in \{X:A\}) \ \& \ \{X:A\} \in K)$ by routine truth-functional moves.

(2) $\{X:A\} \in K \supset ((Z)(Z \in \{X:A\} \equiv A(Z/X)) \ \& \ \{X:A\} \in K)$, from (1) in view of A8.

(3) $(\exists Y)(\{X:A\} \in K \supset ((Z)(Z \in Y \equiv A(Z/X)) \ \& \ Y \in K)$, from (2) by the dual of A7. Then from (3) by routine quantificational moves,

(4) $\{X:A\} \in K \supset (\exists Y)((Z)(Z \in Y \equiv A(Z/X)) \ \& \ Y \in K)$, proving half of Quine's biconditional. On the other hand,

(5) $(Z)(Z \in P \equiv Z \in \{X:A\}) \supset (P \in K \supset \{X:A\} \in K)$ holds by extensionality (A9). Presuming P foreign to $\{X:A\}$ and to K, we derive from (5) by A8,

(6) $(Z)(Z \in P \equiv A(Z/X)) \supset (P \in K \supset \{X:A\} \in K)$. Routine truth-functional and quantificational moves then yield the converse of (4), completing the proof.

(3) The familiar *axiom of Comprehension* is of course provable in T, as follows:[11]

(1) $(Y)(Y \in \{Y:A\} \equiv A)$, by A8 and A10. But then by the dual of A7 and *Modus Ponens*,

(2) $(\exists X)(Y)(Y \in X \equiv A)$, where X is not free in A.

4. Here is installment one of our semantics for T. Let $\mathbf{2} = \{t, f\}$, where t is the truth-value 'true' and f is the truth-value 'false'. A function $\alpha: W \rightarrow \mathbf{2}$ will count as a *general truth-value function for T* provided that the following conditions are fulfilled for all wffs:[12]

(i) $\alpha(\sim A) \neq \alpha(A)$;

(ii) $\alpha(A \supset B) = t$ iff $\alpha(A) = f$ or $\alpha(B) = t$;

(iii) $\alpha((X)A) = t$ iff $\alpha(A(K/X)) = t$ for all terms K of the same type as X;

(iv) $\alpha(K \in \{X:A\}) = \alpha(A(K/X))$

(v) if $\alpha(K \in L) = \alpha(K \in L')$ for all terms K in λ_t, $0 \leqslant t$, $\alpha(L \in M) = \alpha(L' \in M)$ for each M in λ_{t+2}.

A wff A is *true on a general truth-value function* α *for* T if $\alpha(A) = t$.[13] $\mathfrak{S}$ is *generally verifiable in* T if there is a general truth-value function on which every member of $\mathfrak{S}$ is true. If some $\mathfrak{S}'$ isomorphic to $\mathfrak{S}$ is generally verifiable in T, $\mathfrak{S}$ is *weakly generally verifiable*. $\mathfrak{S}$ *generally implies* A (in Tarski's terminology, A is a general consequence of $\mathfrak{S}$) if $\mathfrak{S} \cup \{\sim A\}$ is not weakly generally verifiable. Finally, take A to be *generally valid* if $\emptyset$ generally implies A, or, what comes to the same thing, if A is true on all general truth-value functions for T.[14]

The following lemma will prove useful.

LEMMA 2. Suppose A is generally valid. Then all wffs $A(K/P)$ are generally valid, where K is a term of the same type as P.

PROOF. Let K and P be of the same type t. Let B be an arbitrary wff and α a general truth-value function. We show first that there is a general truth-value function β such that $\alpha(B(K/P)) = \beta(B)$.

Assume first that P does not occur in K (and hence not in $B(K/P)$). Let $P_1, \ldots, P_{i-1}$ be in alphabetical order all the parameters of type t which occur in $B(K/P)$, let P_i be P, and let $P_{i+1}, \ldots$ be the other parameters of type t, again in alphabetical order. Define a function $f: \Pi \rightarrow \rightarrow \Pi - \{P\}$ by setting $f(P_j) = P_{j+1}$ for parameters P_j of type t such that $i \leqslant j$, and $f(Q) = Q$ for all other parameters Q. Note (i) f is an isomorphism in the sense of Section 2, (ii) the set of f-images of wffs of T is the set of wffs to which P is foreign (temporarily baptized $W-$), and (iii) the f-image of $B(K/P)$ is $B(K/P)$. Let $\beta: W \rightarrow \mathbf{2}$ now be defined by cases as follows: (1) if $C \in W-$, and is hence the f-image of a wff D, set $\beta(C) = \alpha(D)$; (2) if P occurs in C, set $\beta(C) = \beta(C(K/P))$, noting that the latter is already defined by (1) since on assumption P is foreign to K. Note too that it follows directly from the fact that α is a general truth-value function that β is one also, since any suspected violation of one of (i)–(v) above by β can be transformed into a violation by α by replacing P by K throughout the suspect context and passing to images under the converse of f. And by definition $\beta(B)=\beta(B(K/P))=\alpha(B(K/P))$, which was to be proved.

Suppose now that P occurs in K. Let Q be a parameter foreign to B and K and of type t. By what has been shown above, there is at any rate a general truth-value function γ such that $\alpha(B(Q/P)(K/Q))=\gamma(B(Q/P))$, since Q is foreign to K. But $B(Q/P)(K/Q)$ is just $B(K/P)$, so $\alpha(B(K/P))= =\gamma(B(Q/P))$. Define $f:\Pi\rightarrow\Pi$ by setting $f(P)=Q, f(Q)=P$, and, for all other parameters R, $f(R)=R$, and then define $\beta(C)=t$ iff the f-image of C is true on γ. Clearly β is a general truth-value function such that $\beta(B)=\gamma(B(Q/P))=\alpha(B(K/P))$, completing the demonstration that for any α we can find a β such that $\alpha(B(K/P))=\beta(B)$.

We complete the proof of Lemma 2 by assuming A generally valid. Suppose for *reductio* that $A(K/P)$ is not generally valid. Then there is a general truth-value function α such that $\alpha(A(K/P))=f$, by our alternate definition of general validity. But by what has been just demonstrated there is then another general truth-value function β such that $\beta(A)=f$, contradicting the assumed general validity of A and ending the proof.

5. We now establish the soundness of our axioms for T, given the semantics of the previous section.

LEMMA 3. Suppose $\vdash A$. Then A is generally valid.

PROOF. We assume that A is a theorem of T and show it true on all general truth-value functions α. Proof is by induction. There are two cases, according as A is an axiom or a consequence of predecessors by *Modus Ponens*. We employ a secondary induction on the number of prefaced universal quantifiers if A is an axiom.

CASE 1. A is an axiom.

1.1. A is not of the form $(X)B$. Then it is of one of the sorts A1–A9. It is readily verified that A is true on arbitrary α. For suppose in particular that A is $(X)(B\supset C)\supset((X)B\supset(X)C)$, and that $(X)(B\supset C)$ and $(X)B$ are both true on α. Then $(B\supset C)(K/X)$ and $B(K/X)$ are both true on α for every term K of T of the same type as X. But $B(K/X)\supset C(K/X)$ is the same as $(B\supset C)(K/X)$. Hence $C(K/X)$ is true on α for all K of the same type as X; hence $(X)C$ is true on α. Or suppose that A is $B\supset(X)B$. Since X cannot occur free in B, $B(K/X)$ is the same as B for all terms K; hence if B is true on α, so is $(X)B$. Finally, note that if A is an extensionality axiom of the sort A9, it is true on α by (v) of Section 4.

1.2. A is of the form $(X)B$. We may assume by the hypothesis of the secondary induction that $B(P/X)$ is generally valid, for some P of the same type as X and foreign to B. But then by Lemma 2, $B(P/X)(K/P)$ is generally valid for all terms K of the type of X; since P is foreign to B, $B(P/X)(K/P)$ is $B(K/X)$ for all such K, and hence $(X)B$ is generally valid by (iii) of Section 4.

CASE 2. A is the consequence of predecessors B and $B \supset A$. Trivial, given the hypothesis of the primary induction, ending the proof of Lemma 3.

LEMMA 4. Suppose $\mathfrak{S}$ is weakly generally verifiable. Then $\mathfrak{S}$ is consistent in T.

PROOF. We prove the lemma first for the case in which $\mathfrak{S}$ is itself generally verifiable. Then there is a general truth-value function α on which all members of $\mathfrak{S}$ are true. Using Lemma 3, one establishes by a straightforward induction on length of derivation that every wff B derivable from $\mathfrak{S}$ is true on α. Since $\vdash A \supset A$ for every A in T, however, by Lemma 3 no wff $\sim(A \supset A)$ is true on α. Hence neither is any such wff derivable from $\mathfrak{S}$, establishing the consistency of generally verifiable $\mathfrak{S}$.

Suppose now that $\mathfrak{S}$ is weakly generally verifiable; then $\mathfrak{S}$ is isomorphic to a generally verifiable $\mathfrak{S}'$; $\mathfrak{S}'$ is consistent by what has been just shown. Assume that $\mathfrak{S}$ is nevertheless inconsistent, for *reductio*. We finish the proof by showing how a derivation of $\sim(A \supset A)$ from $\mathfrak{S}$ can, for some B, be turned into a derivation of $\sim(B \supset B)$ from $\mathfrak{S}'$, a contradiction.

Indeed, by the definition of 'isomorphic' there is a type-preserving one-one mapping f from the parameters of $\mathfrak{S}$ onto the parameters of $\mathfrak{S}'$. For each $C \in W$, let C' be its f-image in the sense of p. 79. Then where $A_1, \ldots, A_n$ is the assumed derivation of $\sim(A \supset A)$ from $\mathfrak{S}$, $A'_1, \ldots, A'_n$ is a derivation of $\sim(A' \supset A')$ from $\mathfrak{S}'$; this is the promised contradiction, completing the proof of the consistency of weakly generally verifiable $\mathfrak{S}$.

COROLLARY. Suppose A is derivable from $\mathfrak{S}$ in T. Then $\mathfrak{S}$ generally implies A.

PROOF. Clearly if $\mathfrak{S} \vdash A$, $\mathfrak{S} \cup \{\sim A\}$ is inconsistent. By the lemma, $\mathfrak{S} \cup \{\sim A\}$ is not weakly generally verifiable, which was to be proved.

6. We turn now to completeness, proving the converses of the lemmas of the previous section. (Proofs in the present section are in large part an adaptation of results in Henkin's [4] and in Section 89 of Beth's [1].)

LEMMA 5. Let $\mathfrak{S}$ be infinitely extendible. If $\mathfrak{S}$ is consistent in T, then $\mathfrak{S}$ is generally verifiable.

PROOF. Suppose $\mathfrak{S}$ is consistent and infinitely extendible. For every i from 1 on, let $(X_i)A_i$ be the alphabetically ith wff of T of the sort $(X)A$; and letting $\mathfrak{S}_0$ be $\mathfrak{S}$, let $\mathfrak{S}_i$ be $\mathfrak{S}_{i-1} \cup \{A_i(P/X_i) \supset (X_i)A_i\}$, where P is the alphabetically earliest parameter of T that is of the same type as X_i and is foreign to $\mathfrak{S}_{i-1}$ and A_i. Let $\mathfrak{S}_\omega$ be the union of $\mathfrak{S}_0$, $\mathfrak{S}_1$, $\mathfrak{S}_2$, ... It is easily verified that $\mathfrak{S}_\omega$ is consistent in T if $\mathfrak{S}$ is, and that, for every wff of T of the sort $(X)A$, there is a parameter (and hence a term) K of T of the same type as X such that $\mathfrak{S}_\omega \vdash A(K/X) \supset (X)A$.

Next, let $\mathfrak{S}^0_\omega$ be $\mathfrak{S}_\omega$; where B_i is the alphabetically ith wff of T, let $\mathfrak{S}^i_\omega$ be $\mathfrak{S}^{i-1}_\omega \cup \{B_i\}$ or $\mathfrak{S}^{i-1}_\omega$ according as $\mathfrak{S}^{i-1}_\omega \cup \{B_i\}$ is consistent or not in T. Let $\mathfrak{S}^\omega_\omega$ be the union of $\mathfrak{S}^0_\omega$, $\mathfrak{S}^1_\omega$, $\mathfrak{S}^2_\omega$, ... It is easily verified that: (a) $\mathfrak{S}^\omega_\omega$ is consistent in T if $\mathfrak{S}_\omega$ (and hence if $\mathfrak{S}$) is; (b) if $\mathfrak{S}^\omega_\omega$ is consistent in T, then (i) $\mathfrak{S}^\omega_\omega \vdash \sim A$ iff it is not the case that $\mathfrak{S}^\omega_\omega \vdash A$, (ii) $\mathfrak{S}^\omega_\omega \vdash A \supset B$ iff it is not the case that $\mathfrak{S}^\omega_\omega \vdash A$ or (it is the case that) $\mathfrak{S}^\omega_\omega \vdash B$, (iii) where X is a variable of T of type t, $0 \leqslant t$, $\mathfrak{S}^\omega_\omega \vdash (X)A$ iff $\mathfrak{S}^\omega_\omega \vdash A(K/X)$ for all terms K of type t.

Let α be the function from the set of wffs of T to $\{t, f\}$ such that, for every A, $\alpha(A) = t$ iff $\mathfrak{S}^\omega_\omega \vdash A$. Since $K \in \{X : A\} \equiv A(K/X)$ is an axiom of T, $\mathfrak{S}^\omega_\omega \vdash K \in \{X : A\} \equiv A(K/X)$; hence $\alpha(K \in \{X : A\} \equiv A(K/X)) = t$, and hence $\alpha(K \in \{X : A\}) = \alpha(A(K/X))$. Applying similar considerations to axioms of the sort A9, we see that if $\alpha(K \in L) = \alpha(K \in L')$ for all terms K in λ_t, $\alpha(L \in M) = \alpha(L' \in M)$ for each M in λ_{t+2}. Hence α meets the conditions (i)–(v) defining a general truth-value function in Section IV. But since $\mathfrak{S}$ is a subset of $\mathfrak{S}^\omega_\omega$, $\mathfrak{S}^\omega_\omega \vdash A$ for every member A of $\mathfrak{S}$. Hence every member of $\mathfrak{S}$ is true on α. Hence every consistent and infinitely extendible set $\mathfrak{S}$ is generally verifiable.

LEMMA 6. For every set $\mathfrak{S}$ of wffs of T, if $\mathfrak{S}$ is consistent in T then $\mathfrak{S}$ is weakly generally verifiable.

PROOF. Let $\mathfrak{S}$ be a consistent set of wffs of T. By Lemma 1, $\mathfrak{S}$ is isomorphic to an infinitely extendible set of wffs $\mathfrak{S}'$. By the argument which concludes the proof of Lemma 4, $\mathfrak{S}'$ is consistent. By Lemma 5, $\mathfrak{S}'$ is generally verifiable; hence $\mathfrak{S}$ is isomorphic to a generally verifiable set of wffs, which was to be proved.

COROLLARY. If $\mathfrak{S}$ generally implies A, $\mathfrak{S} \vdash A$. If A is generally valid, $\vdash A$.

PROOF. We note that the second statement is the specialization of the first to the case $\mathfrak{S}=\emptyset$. Assume then that it is not the case that $\mathfrak{S}\vdash A$. It follows readily that $\mathfrak{S}\cup\{\sim A\}$ is consistent and hence, by the lemma, weakly generally verifiable. So if $\mathfrak{S}\cup\{\sim A\}$ is not weakly generally verifiable, A is derivable from $\mathfrak{S}$ in T, which was to be proved.

We sum up the considerations of this and the preceding section in the following two theorems, which can be thought of as combined soundness and completeness theorems for T:

THEOREM 1. $\mathfrak{S}\vdash A$ if and only if $\mathfrak{S}$ generally implies A.

THEOREM 2. $\vdash A$ if and only if A is generally valid.

II

7. We turn now to comparison and contrast between the semantics presented for T in Section I, which we shall henceforth call *the general truth-value semantics for T*, and a Henkin-style semantics for T, which we shall call *the general model-theoretic semantics for T*.[15] The equivalence of the two semantical approaches yields the following philosophically interesting conclusion: T is consistent with the assumption that the only things which need to be admitted to the range of variables of quantification are those which are nameable in the vocabulary of T.[16] We pause to introduce the requisite model-theoretic notions, beginning with those of *the standard model-theoretic semantics for T*.[17]

8. Let S be a non-empty set.[18] By $\Gamma(S)$, we mean the power set of S – i.e., $\Gamma(S)=\{S':S'\subseteq S\}$. For each non-negative integer t, we define Γ^t recursively as follows: (i) $\Gamma^0(S)=S$; (ii) $\Gamma^{t+1}(S)=\Gamma(\Gamma^t(S))$. $U(S)$ shall be $\bigcup_{t<\omega}\Gamma^t(S)$.[19] Furthermore,

(a) by *the standard system $D(S)$ of domains for T over S*, understand the sequence $\langle\Gamma^0(S),\Gamma^1(S),\Gamma^2(S),\ldots\rangle$;

(b) understand by a *$D(S)$-interpretation of the parameters of T* any function $I:\Pi\rightarrow U(S)$ such that, for each parameter P of type t, $I(P)\in\Gamma^t(S)$;

(c) where I and I' are $D(S)$-interpretations of the parameters of T, and P is a parameter of T, I' will count as a *P-variant* of I if, for every parameter Q of T other than P, $I'(Q)=I(Q)$. (We shall refer to the P-variants of I by '$I^{P\prime}$'.)

(d) where I is a $D(S)$-interpretation of the parameters of T, let *a complete interpretation CI (agreeing with I)* be a function defined on the set λ of terms of T with values in $U(S)$ and on the set W of sentences of T with values in **2**, subject to the following conditions:

(i) $CI(P) = I(P)$;
(ii) $CI(K \in L) = t$ iff $CI(K) \in CI(L)$;
(iii) $CI(\sim A) \neq CI(A)$;
(iv) $CI(A \supset B) = t$ iff $CI(A) = f$ or $CI(B) = t$;
(v) where P is the alphabetically earliest parameter of T of the same type as X that is foreign to A, $CI((X)A) = t$ iff $CI^P(A(P/X)) = t$ for every complete interpretation CI^P agreeing with a P-variant I^P of I;
(vi) where P is as in (v), $CI(\{X:A\}) = \{I^P(P): CI^P(A(P/X)) = t\}$;

(e) by *a standard model for T*, understand any pair $\langle D(S), CI\rangle$, where $D(S)$ is the standard system of domains for T over some non-empty set S, and CI is a complete interpretation of T agreeing with some $D(S)$-interpretation I of the parameters of T;

(f) take a set $\mathfrak{S}$ of wffs of T to be *model-theoretically verifiable* if there is a standard model $\langle D(S), CI\rangle$ for T such that every member of $\mathfrak{S}$ is true on CI (i.e., $CI(A) = t$ for all $A \in \mathfrak{S}$); take $\mathfrak{S}$ to *model-theoretically imply A* if $\mathfrak{S} \cup \{\sim A\}$ is not model-theoretically verifiable, and A to be *valid* if $\emptyset$ model-theoretically implies A.

Despite the crispness which we have attempted to inject into our characterization of the standard model-theoretic semantics for T by stipulations (a)–(f), the reader, who has already been warned in reference 17, will note that the crispness is illusory without specification of the set theory which we are using along with the one, namely T, which we are mentioning. Leaving this choice to the reader (and thus subjecting the choice of what shall eventually count as a standard model for T to the reader's set-theoretical standards), we pass on to an analogous account of Henkin's *general model-theoretic semantics*, adapted here to T.

9. We assume the preliminaries of Section 8. Then

(a) by *a Henkin system $\mathscr{H}(S)$ of domains for T over S*, understand any sequence $\langle S_0, S_1, S_2, \ldots\rangle$, where S_0 is S and where for every t from 0 on, $S_{t+1} \subseteq \Gamma(S_t)$;

(b) understand by *an* $\mathscr{H}(S)$*-interpretation of the parameters of T* any function $I:\Pi\rightarrow U(S)$ such that, for each parameter P of type t, $I(P)\in S_t$;

(c) where I is an $\mathscr{H}(S)$-interpretation of the parameters of T, I^P shall be a *P-variant* of I, defined, *mutatis mutandis*, as in (c) of the preceding section;

(d) where I is an $\mathscr{H}(S)$-interpretation of the parameters of T, let *a complete* $\mathscr{H}(S)$*-interpretation CI (agreeing with I)* be any function defined on the set λ of terms of T with values in $U(S)$ and on the set W of sentences of T with values in **2** which meets the following conditions:

(i)–(vi), as in (d) of the preceding section;

(e) let CI be a complete $\mathscr{H}(S)$ interpretation of T; CI will be called an admissible interpretation provided that, for every t from 0 on and for all terms K of type t, $CI(K)\in S_t$; and $\mathscr{H}(S)$ will be called *a general system of domains* provided that every complete $\mathscr{H}(S)$-interpretation is admissible;

(f) by a general model for T, understand any pair $\langle\mathscr{H}(S), CI\rangle$, where $\mathscr{H}(S)$ is a general system of domains for T and CI is a complete (and hence admissible) $\mathscr{H}(S)$-interpretation; take a set $\mathfrak{S}$ of wffs of T to be *model-theoretically generally verifiable* if there is a general model $\langle\mathscr{H}(S), CI\rangle$ such that every member of $\mathfrak{S}$ is true on CI; define corresponding notions of model-theoretic general implication and of model-theoretic general validity in exact analogy with the definitions of (f) of the last section.

10. We now relate the general model-theoretic semantics of Section 9 to the general truth-value semantics of Section I. Interestingly, model-theoretic general verifiability relates, on the truth-value side, not to general verifiability but to weak general verifiability. (There are indeed sets of wffs which are generally verifiable in the model-theoretic but not in the truth-value sense; cf. [8].) We proceed to the appropriate theorems.[20]

LEMMA 7. Suppose $\mathfrak{S}$ is model-theoretically generally verifiable; then $\mathfrak{S}$ is consistent.

PROOF. As in Lemmas 3 and 4.

We prove the converse of Lemma 7 by showing first that every general truth-value function determines a general model. We shall abbreviate the proof, which is largely an adaptation of a similar result in [5]. By *a canonical system of domains for T*, we mean a Henkin system of domains

$\mathscr{H}(v_0)$, where $v_0 \subseteq \Pi_0$. By a *canonical general model*, we mean a general model $\langle \mathscr{H}(v_0), CI \rangle$.

Let α be a general truth-value function. It is readily verified that the relation '$\leftrightarrow$' defined on Π_0 by

(i) $\quad P \leftrightarrow Q$ iff $\alpha((X)(P \in X \equiv Q \in X)) = t$

is an equivalence relation. Let v_0 be any exhaustive set of representatives of the equivalence classes into which Π_0 is partitioned by $\leftrightarrow$.[21] By *the canonization of* α *relative to* v_0, we mean the pair $Z\alpha = \langle \mathscr{H}(v_0), CI \rangle$, which is defined in accordance with the following specifications:

(ii) for all wffs A of T, $CI(A) = \alpha(A)$;
(iii) if $P \in v_0$, $CI(P) = P$;
(iv) if $P, Q \in \Pi_0$, $CI(P) = CI(Q)$ iff $P \leftrightarrow Q$;
(v) for $t > 0$, if $L \in \lambda_t$ then $CI(L) = \{CI(K) : \alpha(K \in L) = t\}$;
(vi) finally, define $\mathscr{H}(v_0) = \langle S_0, S_1, S_2, \ldots \rangle$ by defining each S_t from 0 on as the set of values of CI for arguments in λ_t.

LEMMA 8. Let α and $Z\alpha = \langle \mathscr{H}(v_0), CI \rangle$ be as above. Then $Z\alpha$ is a canonical general model for T.

PROOF. It suffices to show CI a complete $\mathscr{H}(v_0)$-interpretation of T and to show $\mathscr{H}(v_0)$ a general system of domains. Proof of the former may be had by checking that each of conditions (i)–(vi) of Section 9 (d) is met, proceeding by an induction on length of well-formed formulas. To finish the proof, show $\mathscr{H}(v_0)$ a general system of domains by proving that any $\mathscr{H}(v_0)$-interpretation of the parameters of T can be extended to a complete $\mathscr{H}(v_0)$-interpretation CI'. This is clear if P is a parameter, since $I'(P)$ must be $CI(K)$ for some K. Show then for all wffs A and for all terms L that, where $P_1, \ldots, P_n$ are the parameters in A or L respectively, $I'(P_1) = CI(K_1), \ldots, I'(P_n) = CI(K_n)$, that if A^* is the result of replacing K_1 with $P_1, \ldots, K_n$ with P_n simultaneously throughout A and that if L^* is the result of making similar replacements in L, that $CI(A^*) = CI'(A)$ and $CI(K^*) = CI'(K)$, which completes the proof of the lemma and establishes that $Z\alpha$ is a general model.

LEMMA 9. (Henkin completeness theorem for T.) If $\mathfrak{S}$ is consistent, $\mathfrak{S}$ has a general model; hence $\mathfrak{S}$ is model-theoretically generally verifiable.

PROOF. If $\mathfrak{S}$ is consistent, there is a general truth-value function α on which all members of a set $\mathfrak{S}'$ isomorphic to $\mathfrak{S}$ are true, by Lemma 6. By Lemma 8, all members of $\mathfrak{S}'$ are true on CI, where $Z\alpha = \langle \mathscr{H}(v_0), CI \rangle$ is a canonical general model. Let $f: \Pi \rightarrow \Pi$ be the type-preserving mapping of p. 80 from the parameters of $\mathfrak{S}$ onto those of $\mathfrak{S}'$ (extended if necessary to all of Π by setting $f(P) = P$ if P is foreign to $\mathfrak{S}$). Let $I'(P)$ be defined, for each parameter of T, as $f(I(P))$. It is readily verified that $\langle \mathscr{H}(v_0), CI' \rangle$ is a general model for T and that all members of $\mathfrak{S}$ are true on CI', ending the proof of the lemma.

THEOREM 3. $\mathfrak{S}$ model-theoretically generally implies A if and only if $\mathfrak{S}$ generally implies A.

THEOREM 4. A is model-theoretically generally valid if and only if A is generally valid.

PROOF by Theorems 1 and 2, Lemmas 7 and 9, and definitions.

III

11. We now address ourselves to the problem of constructing *a standard truth-value semantics for T*. We warn the reader, however, that although in our opinion the general truth-value semantics of Section I offers ontological and perhaps conceptual economies over against the general model-theoretic semantics of Section 9, no similar economies are to be sought in this part. But if one's model-theoretic view of truth-value semantics is that the range of the quantifiers has been restricted to those entities actually *named* (on a given interpretation) by terms of our type-theoretic language, a view implicit in the treatment of the universal quantifier in (iii) of Section 4, then it would seem that one could simulate any standard model for T if one makes provision in one's truth-value semantics for the addition of an appropriately large supply of names. One must, of course, also lay down conditions which insure that all entities of the model do, in effect, receive names. As noted, this is not an economical procedure; it is the work of Section I, not that of this part, that we commend to those of thrifty philosophic inclination. On the other hand, it is of interest to think from a more freewheeling point of view about what it takes to build a truth-value semantics equivalent to the (standard) model-theoretic account of section 8. Although we make no claim that the particular stipulations which we have chosen are the most economical or interesting, they are reasonably direct. Given a mod-

icum of indulgence toward our propensity to presume that a set (e.g., of parameters) is well ordered, we shall prove them sufficient.

12. Syntactical preliminaries are as in Section 2. A *parametric extension of T* is like T except for containing zero or more additional parameters. We shall refer to parametric extensions of T by 'T^*'; to the sets of sentences, parameters, terms, parameters of type t, and terms of type t respectively for a given T^* by 'W^*', 'Π^*', 'λ^*', 'Π_t^*', and 'λ_t^*', extending in a natural way the conventions of Section I. Similarly, define *a general truth-value function for* T^*, *mutatis mutandis*, as in Section 4.

13. Installment two of our truth-value semantics for T follows. Let T^* be a parametric extension of T and let α be a general truth-value function for T^*. α will be called *a truth-value function for* T^* provided that, in addition to (i)–(v) of Section 4, the following three conditions are fulfilled.[22]

(vi) There exists a sequence $v = \langle v_0, v_1, v_2, \ldots \rangle$, where
(a) for every type t, $v_t \subseteq \Pi_t^*$;
(b) for every type t, if v_t has exactly n members (where n may be finite or infinite), v_{t+1} has 2^n members;
(c) v_0 is non-empty.

(vii) The sequence v (of sets of parameters of T^*) being as in (vi), there exists for each t from 1 on a one-one mapping f_t from v_t onto $\Gamma(v_{t-1})$, such that for any parameter Q of v_{t-1} and R of v_t, $\alpha(Q \in R) = t$ iff $Q \in f_t(R)$.

(viii) There exists, for each t from 0 on, a function g_t from λ_t^* to v_t, where v_t is as in (vi), such that
(a) if $K \in v_t$, $g_t(K) = K$;
(b) if K and L are of consecutively ascending types t and $t+1$ respectively, then
$\alpha(K \in L) = \alpha(g_t(K) \in g_{t+1}(L))$.

If T^* is a parametric extension of T and α is a truth-value function for T^*, we say that a wff A of T^* is *true on* α if $\alpha(A) = t$. If $\mathfrak{S}$ is a set of wffs of T and A is a wff of T, we shall say that (1) $\mathfrak{S}$ is *verifiable* if, for some parametric extension T^* of T and some truth-value function α for T^*, every member of $\mathfrak{S}$ is true in α; (2) $\mathfrak{S}$ *implies* A if $\mathfrak{S} \cup \{\sim A\}$ is not verifiable; and (3) A is *valid* if $\{\sim A\}$ is not verifiable (alternatively, and equivalently, if A is true on all truth-value functions α).

14. It may be obvious that the model-theoretic notions of 8 coincide with their analogues in 13, in the sense that a set $\mathfrak{S}$ of wffs of T is verifiable iff model-theoretically verifiable, etc. As suggested in our initial motivating remarks, conditions (vi)–(viii) have been incorporated into the characterization of a truth-value function to have just this effect. For conditions (vi) and (vii) assure that each member of v_0 may be viewed as a (non-redundant) name of a particular member of a given non-empty set S; similarly, for $0<t$ the members of v_t are names of sets – specifically, each names, again non-redundantly, a member of $\Gamma^t(S)$, while conversely each member of $\Gamma^t(S)$ is named by one and only one parameter in v_t. Accordingly the sequence v of (vi) simulates the *standard* system of domains $D(S)$ over S.

On the other hand, condition (viii) of the last section assures that each term of T^* *not* in the v_t of its type will be redundant; for by (b) under (viii), the systematic replacement of any such term K by $g_t(K)$ will not affect truth-values; hence K may be viewed as a synonym of $g_t(K)$, naming the same item in an associated standard model. So though our quantifier (and, by the way, our abstraction operator) continues to look at names and not at things, all the things which one takes to exist in a model-theoretic standard interpretation of type theory may be *viewed* as named on some truth-value function. We turn now to proofs.

15. Let T^* be a parametric extension of T. Extending the definitions of 8 *mutatis mutandis* to T^*, let $\langle D(S), CI^*\rangle = M$ be a standard model for T^*. M will be called *full* provided that the restriction of CI^* to a given Π_t^* is *onto* $\Gamma^t(S)$, for all types t. (In terms of our motivating remarks, a model is full if each type-theoretic entity of the model has a name among the parameters of T^*.)

Call two models *T-equivalent* if they make the same wffs of T true. The following lemmas are trivial.

LEMMA 10. Let $M=\langle D(S), CI\rangle$ be a standard model for T. Then for some parametric extension T^* of T, there is a T-equivalent full model M^*. (For proof, add a new parameter P of type t for each item in $\Gamma^t(S)$ and for every type t, and extend CI in obvious fashion.)

LEMMA 11. Let $M^* = \langle D(S), CI^* \rangle$ be a standard model for T^*. Let CI be the restriction of CI^* to terms and wffs of T. $M = \langle D(S), CI \rangle$ is a standard model for T and is T-equivalent to M^*. (Proof obvious.)

Let T^* be a parametric extension of T, and let v_0 be a (non-empty) subset of Π_0^*. $M_c = \langle D(v_0), CI \rangle$ will be called a *normal canonical model for* T^* provided that the following conditions are fulfilled:

(1) M_c is a standard model for T^*;

(2) M_c is full;

(3) for all $P \in v_0$, $CI(P) = P$.

Let M and M' be full standard models for T^*, where M is $\langle D(S), CI \rangle$ and M' is $\langle D(S'), CI' \rangle$. For every type t, let h_t be a bijection from $\Gamma^t(S)$ onto $\Gamma^t(S')$; for each term K in λ_t^*, let $CI'(K)$ be $h_t(CI(K))$; for all wffs A, let $CI(A) = CI'(A)$. If all of these conditions can be fulfilled, we call M and M' *isomorphic*.

LEMMA 12. Every full standard model M for T^* is isomorphic to a normal canonical model M_c for T^*.

PROOF. Let $M = \langle D(S), CI \rangle$ be a full standard model for T^*; we give a recipe for an isomorphic normal canonical model. The relation of having the same value under CI partitions the members of Π_0^* into equivalence classes; let P be a member of v_0 iff it is an alphabetically first member of its equivalence class. Set $h_0(P) = CI(P)$, for each $P \in v_0$. h_t having been defined on all members of $\Gamma^t(v_0)$, if $r \in \Gamma^{t+1}(v_0)$, let $h_{t+1}(r) = \{h_t(q) : q \in r\}$. Clearly each of the h_t is a one-one correspondence from $\Gamma^t(v_0)$ to $\Gamma^t(S)$.

For each parameter P of Π_t^*, let $I'(P) = h_t^\circ(CI(P))$, where h° is the inverse of h. It is then readily verified that $\langle D(v_0), CI' \rangle$ is a normal canonical model isomorphic to M. In particular, (2) holds of it since M is full; (3), by the definition of v_0 and of h_0.

COROLLARY. A set $\mathfrak{S}$ of wffs of T is model-theoretically verifiable iff there is a normal canonical model $M_c = \langle D(v_0), CI \rangle$ for some parametric extension T^* of T such that $CI(A) = t$ for every A in $\mathfrak{S}$.

PROOF. If $\mathfrak{S}$ has a model, by Lemmas 10 and 12 $\mathfrak{S}$ has a normal canonical model M_c for some T^*; conversely, by Lemma 11 a normal canonical model for T^* is T-equivalent to some standard model for T, completing the proof of the corollary.

We now show that normal canonical models determine truth-value functions.

LEMMA 13. Let $M = \langle D(v_0), CI \rangle$ be a normal canonical model for a parametric extension T^* of T. Then the restriction of CI to sentences is a truth-value function.

PROOF. We must show that conditions (i)–(v) of 4 and (vi)–(viii) of 13 are fulfilled by CI for T^*. That CI meets (i) and (ii) is obvious, given the definition of a complete interpretation in (d) of Section 8. To prove (iii), it suffices to recall that M is full. Hence $A(K/X)$ is true for all terms K of the same type as X iff $A(P/X)$ is true for all parameters P of that type on CI, since there is sure to be a parameter P such that $CI(K)=CI(P)$ for each term K. But $A(P/X)$ is true for all parameters P of the same type as X iff $(X)A$ is true on CI, since among the $CI(P)$ are *all* items of the appropriate level. (iv) and (v) hold respectively by items (ii) and (vi) under (d) of Section 8 and by the principle of extensionality for sets.

To prove (vi), choose v_0 itself as the first member of the sequence v; for $t>0$, let a parameter P of type t be a member of v_t iff for every alphabetic predecessor Q of type t of P, $CI(P)\neq CI(Q)$; clearly each v_t is in one-one correspondence with $\Gamma^t(v_0)$. To find the mappings f_t required by (vii), let I_t be the restriction of CI to members of v_t and let I_t^{-1} be the inverse image of I_t: i.e., the function $h:\Gamma^{t+1}(v_0)\to\Gamma(v_t)$ such that $Q\in h(s)$ iff $I^t(Q)\in s$. Then for each t from 0 on, define $f_{t+1}:v_{t+1}\to\Gamma(v_t)$ by setting $f_{t+1}(P)=I_t^{-1}(I_{t+1}(P))$. It is then clear that CI meets condition (vii), since the following equivalence follow from definitions for all $Q\in v_t$ and $R\in v_{t+1}$:

$$CI(Q\in R)=t\Leftrightarrow CI(Q)\in CI(R)\Leftrightarrow I_t(Q)\in I_{t+1}(R)\Leftrightarrow$$
$$Q\in I_t^{-1}(I_{t+1}(R))\Leftrightarrow Q\in f_{t+1}(R);$$

furthermore, since each I_t is a one-one correspondence so is each f_{t+1}.

Finally, for each term K in λ_t^*, let $g_t(K)$ be the unique parameter P of type t in v_t such that $CI(K)=CI(P)$; because M is full there must be such a P. Accordingly condition (viii) holds. This completes the proof of Lemma 13.

We have just seen that normal canonical models straightforwardly determine truth-value functions. We now prove the converse. Where α is a truth-value function for T^*, we shall define its *normal canonization* $Z_v\alpha$ by building on the work of Section II.

Suppose then that α is a truth-value function. Let the sequence $v = \langle v_0, v_1, v_2, \ldots \rangle$, the functions f_t, and the functions g_t be those whose existence is guaranteed by (vi)–(viii) of Section 13. By the normal canonization $Z_v\alpha$ of α (relative to v), we mean the pair $\langle D(v_0), CI \rangle$, where $D(v_0)$ is the standard system of domains over the initial set v_0 in the sequence v, and CI agrees with α on sentences of T^* and is defined as follows on terms:

(1) if $P \in v_0$, $CI(P) = P$;
(2) if $P \in v_{t+1}$, $CI(P) = \{CI(Q) : Q \in f_{t+1}(P)\}$;
(3) if K is a term of T^* of type t, $CI(K) = CI(g_t(K))$.

It is readily verified that (1)–(3) serve to define inductively CI for each term of T^*. Here is the converse of Lemma 13 (and the analogue of Lemma 8 for the standard type-theoretic semantics).

LEMMA 14. Let α be a truth-value function for a parametric extension T^* of T, and let $Z_v\alpha = \langle D(v_0), CI \rangle$ be the normal canonization of α just defined. Then $Z_v\alpha$ is a normal canonical model for T^*.

PROOF. To show that $Z_v\alpha$ is a normal canonical model, it clearly suffices to show that it is a full standard model. We first show $Z_v\alpha$ full, assuming on inductive hypothesis for $t < i$ that every member of $\Gamma^t(v_0)$ is the image under CI of some parameter P in v_t (and hence of some parameter in Π_t^*) and showing that this statement remains true when $t = i$. We note that this is clear if $i = 0$, since $CI(P) = P$ for all P in v_0 by (1) above.

Suppose now that $0 < i$. Let s be an arbitrary member of $\Gamma^i(v_0)$. On inductive hypothesis, each member s_j of s is the image under CI of some parameter Q_j in v_{i-1}. But there is by (vii) of Section 13 some parameter P in v_i such that $f_i(P) = \{Q_j : CI(Q_j) \in s\}$. But then by (2) above $CI(P) = s$. This completes the inductive argument and shows $Z_v\alpha$ full.

We must now show $Z_v\alpha$ a standard model. For this it will suffice to show CI a complete interpretation in the sense of (d) of Section 8, since by definition $D(v_0)$ is a standard system of domains. Since the strategy is essentially that lately employed in proving Lemma 8, we can safely leave most of this task to the reader. Inasmuch as we have carried the abstraction notation into this part (via the syntactical preliminaries) while ignoring it in practice, we at least owe it to the reader to make it plausible that (3) above correctly defines CI on abstracts. We do this by showing that every sentence of T^* of the form

(4) $(X)(X \in \{Y:A\} \equiv X \in P)$, where P is $g_t(\{Y:A\})$, is true on α.

In fact if (4) is not true on α, there is by definition of a truth-value function some term K of type $t-1$ such that $\alpha(K \in \{Y:A\}) \neq \alpha(K \in P)$. But by (b) under (viii) of Section 13, $\alpha(K \in \{Y:A\}) = \alpha(g_{t-1}(K) \in g_t\{Y:A\})$ and $\alpha(K \in P) = \alpha(g_{t-1}(K) \in g_t(P))$. But on assumption and by 13 (viii) (a), $g_t\{Y:A\} = g_t(P) = P$, which shows that there is no term K which refutes (4); hence (4) is true on α. Entrusting other details to the reader, we pronounce $Z_v\alpha$ a standard, and hence by what has already been shown a normal canonical, model for T^*.

We have proved enough lemmas.

THEOREM 5. Let $\mathfrak{S}$ be a set of wffs of T. Then $\mathfrak{S}$ is verifiable if and only if $\mathfrak{S}$ is model-theoretically verifiable.

PROOF. Suppose $\mathfrak{S}$ is verifiable. Then there is a truth-value function α on which every member of $\mathfrak{S}$ is true, for some parametric extension T^* of T. By Lemma 14 there is a normal canonical model $\langle D(v_0), CI\rangle$ such that CI agrees with α on sentences of T^*; by the Corollary to Lemma 12, $\mathfrak{S}$ is model-theoretically verifiable.

Suppose on the other hand that $\mathfrak{S}$ is model-theoretically verifiable. Again by the Corollary to Lemma 12, there is a normal canonical model $\langle D(v_0), CI\rangle$ for a parametric extension T^* of T such that every member of $\mathfrak{S}$ is true on CI. But by Lemma 13, the restriction of CI to sentences of T^* is a truth-value function. Hence $\mathfrak{S}$ is verifiable, completing the proof of the theorem.

THEOREM 6. Let $\mathfrak{S}$ be a set of sentences of T and A be a sentence of T.

(a) $\mathfrak{S}$ model-theoretically implies A iff $\mathfrak{S}$ implies A;
(b) A is model-theoretically valid iff A is valid.

PROOF by Theorem 5 and definitions.
This completes the proof of our principal theorems.

16. In conclusion, we should like to remark that both the standard and the general versions of our truth-value semantics are easily adapted to variations on the syntactical or the semantic side. In particular, type-theoretic versions of the axioms of infinity and choice are easily accommodated (the latter perhaps particularly appropriate in view of our

relaxed attitude toward the use of that axiom in the last part), while on the other hand one may drop the axioms of extensionality if one wishes; one might even drop the axioms of specification (A6 and A7) to get a *free* type theory in the sense of Lambert (cf. his own contribution to this volume).

Of perhaps greater interest is the question whether one can modify the account of a general truth-value function in 4 in such a way that the truth-value of a given sentence would be fixed when (a) the truth-values of all shorter sentences are fixed. (We could recast our account of a truth-value function rather easily to meet condition (a), since on that account the truth-value of a sentence $(X)A$ is in fact fixed when the truth-value of $A(P/X)$ is fixed for every parameter P of appropriate type; but as we have noted above abstracts are essentially along for the ride in our standard truth-value semantics, for that story would remain about the same if the abstraction machinery were dropped. On the other hand, abstracts play a crucial role in our general truth-value semantics, as we shall immediately demonstrate.)

OBSERVATION ω. There is a general truth-value function α and a formula $(X)A$ such that (1) all sentences $A(K/X)$ shorter than $(X)A$ are true on α, but (2) $(X)A$ is false on α.

PROOF. Let q be the set whose only member is Quine, and let $D(q)$ be the standard system of domains for T over q.[22] Define an interpretation I of the parameters of T by setting $I(P)=$ Quine for all parameters of type 0; if $0<t$ and P is of type t, let $I(P)=\Gamma^{t-1}(q)$, for all types t and parameters P. Let $\langle D(q), CI\rangle$ be the (standard, and hence general) model determined by I.

Let α be the restriction of CI to wffs. Then α is a general truth-value function. To show this, it will suffice to show that for every t, if $s\in\Gamma^t(q)$ then $s=CI(K)$ for some K in λ_t. (Informally, what we are showing is that on each level in this particular model all sets are named by some term of T; in fact this must hold for any general model such that (i) the level zero set is finite and (ii) all members of the level zero set have names, since under these circumstances the sets of any level must also be finite and in fact have names; we remark moreover that perforce any general model satisfying (i) is a standard model.)

Returning to our immediate task, let us establish by induction on i that for every s, if $s\in\Gamma^i(q)$, $CI(K)=s$ for some K in λ_i. This is clear if $i=0$, for *all* of our $\aleph_0$ parameters of type zero have been temporarily set aside as names of Quine.[23] Supposing our proposition true for arbitrary i, we prove it for $i+1$.

Let s then belong to $\Gamma^{i+1}(q)$; i.e., $s \subseteq \Gamma^i(q)$. $\Gamma^i(q)$, as noted, is finite. Accordingly we may informally specify s as $\{x : x \in \Gamma^i(q) \,\&\, (x = s_1 \vee \vee x = s_2 \vee \cdots \vee x = s_n)\}$, where $s_1, \ldots, s_n$ are all the members of s (and substituting $x \neq x$ for the parenthesized condition if s is empty). Where X is a variable of type i, Y is a variable of type $i+1$, and employing the inductive hypothesis, let K_s be $\{X : (Y)\,(X \in Y \equiv K_1 \in Y) \vee \cdots \vee (Y)\,(X \in Y \equiv \equiv K_n \in Y)\}$, where $CI(K) = s_1$ and ... and $CI(K_n) = s_n$ when $s_1, \ldots, s_n$ are the members of s; when s is empty, let K_s be $\{X : \sim (A \supset A)\}$, where A is the alphabetically first sentence of T. In view of the extensionality axioms, it is clear that $CI(K_s) = s$, completing the inductive argument.

It is then easy to go on to show, in the spirit of Lemma 13, that α is a general truth-value function. We now confirm observation ω. For let A be $P \in X$, where P and X are respectively of types 0 and 1. $(X)A$ is not true on α, since Quine is not a member of the null set. But $A(K/X)$ is true when K is a parameter, since for all type 1 parameters Q, $CI(Q) = q$. But only when K is a parameter is $A(K/X)$ shorter than $(X)A$. Q.E.D.

The observation has an interesting corollary.[24]

OBSERVATION $\omega+1$. There are two distinct general truth-value functions α and β which agree on all sentences of T in which no abstracts or quantifiers occur.

PROOF. Let $\langle D(q), CI \rangle$ be as in the preceding observation, and let α again be the restriction of CI to sentences. Let $r = \{0, 1\}$. Let $CI'(P) = 0$ for the alphabetically first parameter of Π_0; otherwise if $Q \in \Pi_0$, $CI'(Q) = 1$. If $0 < t$, let $CI'(R) = \Gamma^{t-1}(r)$ for each parameter R in Π_t. Arguing as above, note that the extension of CI' to a complete $D(r)$-interpretation yields a standard model $\langle D(r), CI' \rangle$, and that the restriction of CI' to wffs of T is a general truth-value function β. Clearly all sentences of T in which neither connectives nor quantifiers nor abstracts occur are true both on α and on β, whence α and β agree on sentences free of both quantifiers and abstracts. On the other hand, where X and Y are of type 0 and Z is of type 1, the sentence $\exists X \exists Y \exists Z (X \in Z \,\&\, \sim (Y \in Z))$ is true on β but not on α.

Although the observations just made are relatively trivial, that they can be made at all suggests that truth-value semantics may be more than just a recasting of model-theoretic semantics. In Section I of this paper, and in the earlier papers of Leblanc cited therein, proof was given that truth-value semantics can be accommodated to those systems of logic for which *bona fide* completeness results may be obtained from the model-theoretic viewpoint. What we should like to see in addition are results which show truth-value semantics to have a life of its own, not necessarily dependent on the model-theoretic insights from which it arose and into which, as we have showed, it can for certain purposes be translated. Noting that one of the abiding purposes of modern logical research has been the reduction of facts about "things" to facts about appropriately constructed formal languages, we welcome the increasing interest of recent years in one or another form of what we have called 'truth-value semantics' and trust that it may herald genuinely deeper insights into, among other things, the theory of types.

Temple University

Indiana University

BIBLIOGRAPHY

[1] E. W. Beth, *The Foundations of Mathematics*, Amsterdam 1959.
[2] A. Church, *Introduction to Mathematical Logic*, vol. I, Princeton 1956.
[3] F. B. Fitch, 'Intuitionistic Modal Logic with Quantifiers', *Portugaliae Mathematica* 7 (1948) 113–118.
[4] L. Henkin, 'The Completeness of the First-Order Functional Calculus', *The Journal of Symbolic Logic* **14** (1949) 159–66.
[5] L. Henkin, 'Completeness in the Theory of Types', *The Journal of Symbolic Logic* **15** (1950) 81–91.
[6] L. Henkin, 'Banishing the Rule of Substitution for Functional Variables', *The Journal of Symbolic Logic* **18** (1953) 201–208.
[7] K. J. J. Hintikka, 'Two Papers on Symbolic Logic', *Acta Philosophica Fennica* **8** (1955).
[8] H. Leblanc, 'A simplified account of validity and implication', *The Journal of Symbolic Logic* **33** (1968) 231–235.
[9] H. Leblanc, 'A Simplified Strong Completeness Proof for $QC=$', forthcoming.
[10] H. Leblanc, 'Three generalizations of a theorem of Beth's', forthcoming.
[11] W. V. O. Quine, *Set Theory and its Logic*, Cambridge, 1963.
[12] K. Schütte, 'Syntactical and semantical properties of simple type theory', *The Journal of Symbolic Logic* **25** (1960) 305–26.

REFERENCES

[1] See [8], [9], and [10].

[2] Parameters and variables will play here the roles respectively assigned elsewhere to free variables and bound ones. By using two runs of letters per type, we avoid some of the difficulties that would otherwise be involved in giving a correct account of substitution (of terms) for free variables. Neither our parameters nor our variables are to be associated with relations of more than one argument; as in [11], such relations may be simulated using the well-known Wiener-Kuratowski techniques.

[3] Define the *simultaneous replacement* of $P_1, \ldots, P_n$ by $Q_1, \ldots, Q_n$ in A as $A(R_1/P_1)(\ldots)(R_n/P_n)(Q_1/R_1)(\ldots)(Q_n/R_n)$, where $R_1, \ldots, R_n$ are the first n parameters foreign to A and different from $Q_1, \ldots, Q_n$.

[4] The technique of the papers of Leblanc cited earlier has been revised here to make the relation 'is isomorphic to' an equivalence relation among sets of wffs of T. Note that if $\mathfrak{S}$ contains no parameters (in particular, if $\mathfrak{S}$ is empty), every set isomorphic to $\mathfrak{S}$ is identical with $\mathfrak{S}$ by our definitions (since f is here the empty function). We shall, by the way, refer to f itself as an *isomorphism*, if it meets the conditions laid down in the text.

[5] We presume '&', '$\wedge$', '$\equiv$', and '$\exists$' defined in the customary manner. Note that only sentences are axioms.

[6] We might dispense with the braces and colon as primitive signs, following rather Quine's example in [11] by defining $P \in \{X:A\}$ as $A(P/X)$ and $\{X:A\} \in K$ as $(\exists Y)((Z)(Z \in Y \equiv A(Z/X))\ \&\ Y \in K)$. In that case A7 could be replaced by the *axiom* (scheme) *of Comprehension*, $(\exists X)(Y)(Y \in X \equiv A)$, where X is not free in A. However, because of the crucial role played by abstracts in our account of a general truth-value function for T, we prefer to have $P \in \{X:A\}$ and $\{X:A\} \in K$ count as genuine wffs of T (rather than as mere definitional rewrites)

[7] If X is not free in A, $A(K/X)$ is not of course just A.

[8] This is the familiar *axiom of Extensionality*. It may of course be dropped (as it is, e.g., in [12]), turning T into a theory of attributes rather than of classes. If A9 is dropped, then in the semantical account of Section 4, (v) must also be dropped.

[9] The trick of counting $(X)A(X/P)$ as an axiom when A is an axiom stems from [3].

[10] Analogous moves will show that the biconditional in question can do duty for A9.

[11] This proof borrows from [6], p. 203.

[12] Note that a general truth-value function is not "recursive" in the sense that the truth-values of longer sentences be invariably determined by the truth-values of shorter ones; cf. the observation of p. 97.

[13] The ambiguity of our use of 't' for 'true' as well as for an unspecified type is, of course, harmlessly resolved in context.

[14] The above account of general implication and validity adapts to T the suggestion of Professor Hintikka to Leblanc acknowledged at the outset. Cf. [9] on the matter.

[15] Our account below borrows significantly from [5], [4], and from Section 53 of [2].

[16] We are partially indebted to Professor John Corcoran for this way of putting the matter.

[17] In view of the Gödel result cited on p. 77, completeness proofs (and hence the possibility of sharp syntactic characterization of semantical concepts which such proofs afford) are out of the question when we turn to the standard model-theoretic semantics for T. Accordingly, although the account below summarizes what we take to be intended by the standard model theory for T, as do corresponding accounts in [5] and (for the second-order calculus) in [2], the standards involved seem to us as little secure as is the gold standard nowadays.

[18] We have long since lost interest in ill-formed formulas, which frees the letter 'S' to refer (henceforth) to arbitrary sets; we use 's', and on occasion 'q' and 'r', for the same purpose. '$\mathfrak{S}$' continues to refer to sets of *sentences*.
[19] $U(S)$ is thus the type-theoretic (standard) *universe* over S, while each of the $\Gamma^t(S)$ is the collection of all type-theoretic entities of level t. On the intended interpretation, $\Gamma^0(S)$ – i.e., S itself – is of course a collection of individuals, which do not themselves have further members. ($U(S)$, naturally, is unmentionable according to the canons of simple type theory itself.)
[20] For the remainder of this section, we leave most of the details in carrying out proofs to the reader.
[21] I.e., ν_0 contains exactly one parameter from each equivalence class. One may, of course, specify a unique ν_0 for any α by requiring that each equivalence class be represented by its alphabetically first member.
[22] We distinguish q from its illustrious member, despite the reluctance which he has showed in [11] and elsewhere to do so.
[23] The reader who thinks this unduly profligate may, if he wishes, decrease temporarily the number of parameters of T for each given type to finite size; in order to preserve the uniformity of our account of a general truth-value function for T, however, we shall not do so.
[24] The question which the corollary answers was put to us by Professor Nuel Belnap.

J. M. VICKERS

PROBABILITY AND NON STANDARD LOGICS*

I. BELIEF, REASONABLENESS AND PROBABILITY

In *The Logical Foundations of Probability* [1] Carnap develops a theory of probability based on classical predicate logic in which probability is treated as a generalization of logic. In this respect Carnap's theory is in the tradition of the classical probability theorists, notably La Place and Hume,[2] for in the classical theorie probability is considered to be the proportion of possible cases in which a proposition is true, and is thus a generalization of the logical concept of validity, or truth in all possible cases, and consistency, or truth in some possible case. Hume's account differs slightly but importantly: in it probability is related to inference and the logical concept of implication is generalized. On this theory the probability of a proposition relative to a set of premises is the proportion of extensions of the premises in which the conclusion holds. Carnap's confirmation functions are defined in this way too, where the requisite logical concepts are those of predicate logic, and his account differs from the classical theorists – apart from the additional precision available through the use of advanced logical techniques – mainly in the role played by the principle of indifference. This principle asserts that distinct atomic cases are equiprobable. The classical theorists accepted it [3] and Carnap makes use of it for *a priori* measures only in restricted ways.

The principle of indifference is said to lead to inconsistencies because it may give different probabilities for the same event when the possible cases are differently described. Thus if every ball is either black or white, and every bag includes two balls, the probability of drawing a bag of two white balls is either 1/2 or 1/3, depending upon whether or not we take account of the order of the balls in the bag.

One need not cherish the principle of indifference to see that this difficulty depends not so much upon it, as upon making use of a relative notion of probability, which depends upon the notion of *possible case*, as if it did not have this dependence. The same sorts of confusions could

K. Lambert (ed.), Philosophical Problems in Logic.

arise if we were not explicit about the way in which validity depends upon a characterization of models: A proposition which has counter-instances in models of one sort may be valid when models are more restricted. In just this way, once it is settled what is and what is not a possible case, the principle of indifference is quite unequivocal about assigning probabilities, so long as the appropriate limits exist. We are by now accustomed to different probabilities in statistical mechanics for different sorts of particles, and this phenomenon can I think best be understood as a consequence of the correct physical model not being uniquely determined.

Another account of probability by which Carnap has been influenced, especially since 1960,[4] is the psychological or epistemic account, due originally to Ramsey and (independently) de Finetti.[5] Ramsey's theory depends upon the practical exercise of reason, and is primilary an account of partial belief. The strength of a man's belief in a proposition is taken to be the odds at which he will bet on it. On this view of partial belief it is plausible to think of the laws of probability as normative strictures defining *reasonableness* of belief. This account is particularly appealing in view of results which show that a set of partial beliefs is probabilistic just in case it is *coherent*,[6] i.e. just in case for any set of bets in accordance with the beliefs, there is some eventuation in which the bettor is not a net loser. Thus one is invited to think of belief as disposition to bet, and of unreasonable belief as disposition to bet with no chance of winning. If we do think this way, then unreasonable belief is non-probabilistic belief, and the laws of probability take on the status of laws of reasonable thought, thus becoming in a quite clear sense laws of logic.

There is, however, the following problem with this theory: It is not at all clear what would constitute acting in accordance with an incoherent set of beliefs. If a man gives odds for and against a proposition it is much more sensible to suppose that he did not understand the terms of the bet than it is to suppose that he is both more and less inclined to think that it will happen than that it would not. Indeed, this difficulty is endemic and it is not hard to show on the usual assumptions that so long as a man is not willing to give away outright what he values, then his betting function is coherent.[7] Thus it is not easy to see how coherence theories can separate rationality from belief without taking an agent's beliefs to be irrational only when we fail to understand them.

Thus the identification of reasonableness with coherence does not let us see how to make sense of unreasonable belief. In Carnap's liaison with psychological theories of probability.[8] he leaves open the option of taking partial belief to be always probabilistic and of placing additional restrictions, such as symmetry, upon reasonable belief. The arguments for the additional restrictions are not as compelling as one would like, however, largely because they involve essential reference to the ways in which beliefs do or should change over time, and are thus involved in questions of projectability, which questions have as yet no apparent resolution within the framework of Carnapian inductive logic.[9] Nor is it clear that we should have to look at the problem of belief changes before considering the question of reasonableness or giving a consistent description of unreasonable belief.

Further, in at least one restricted case, under certain plausible assumptions we can argue that no probabilistic set of beliefs is unreasonable. Let me do that now.

When we apply the laws of probability to beliefs we make use of notions of *necessity* and *necessary exclusion* in order to phrase the laws.

(i) If A is necessary then $p(A)=1$

(ii) If A and B are necessarily exclusive then $p(A \vee B)=p(A)+p(B)$

If we interpret necessity in these laws as truth-functional tautologousness we get a weaker theory than that in which it is interpreted as first-order validity, for example. For the moment let us restrict consideration to the first of these theories and call it *truth-functional probability*.

We can associate with each notion of reasonableness of belief, a restriction, a way of counting certain functions as unreasonable, or, as we shall say, of *excluding* these functions. (We need not suppose that each notion of reasonableness gives sufficient conditions for belief functions being reasonable, it is enough to agree that some necessary conditions are always entailed.) If such a restriction can be phrased without attributing to the objects of belief any more than a truth-functional structure, then we shall say that it is a *truth-functional restriction*. Thus the restriction

(iii) if p is a reasonable belief function then for all propositions A and B $p(A \wedge B) \leqslant p(A)$

is truth functional but the restriction

(iv) If p is a reasonable belief function then for all properties F and all individuals a $p(Fa) \leqslant p(\exists xFx)$

is not.

Suppose now we consider truth-functional probability measures defined over collections of propositions where

(v) There are propositions $A_1, \ldots, A_k$ in the collection which are logically independent. Thus the *atoms*, conjuncts including for each A_i either it or its negation but not both, are consistent.

(vi) Every proposition in the space can be given as the disjunction of atoms.

And for simplicity we suppose all truth-functional measures to be of this sort. (The point of the argument is made well enough without generalization to infinite sets.)

Among all the measures on such a set will be some *two-valued* measures, which assign 1 to every proposition implied by some atom and 0 to every other proposition. Further, any measure on the set can be given as a normalized weighting of two-valued functions, and, of course, every normalization of two valued-functions is probabilistic.

Now with respect to restrictions of reasonableness we can make two points.

First, since the atoms are given in terms of truth-functional structure, no adequate truth-functional restriction can exclude any atom unless it excludes all atoms. For if an atom is excluded and another is not, we can easily relabel propositions (using double negation, for example) in such a way that the two atoms are isomorphic, and are thus not distinguishable as far as truth-functional logic is concerned.

Second, the procedure of forming functions by normalized weightings of given functions does not introduce unreasonableness. Thus if a function is formed by normalized weighting of given functions, and some adequate truth-functional restriction excludes the former, it must also exclude some of the latter.

From these it follows that no adequate truth-functional restriction can exclude any truth-functional probability measure. An interesting corollary is that if there is an adequate rule of detachment for inductive logic which is not implied by the laws of probability (where these laws have as consequences that all tautologies are assigned probability 1 and that probability is additive over the disjunction of tautologically exclusive propositions) then that rule cannot be phrased in terms of the propositional structure of objects believed.

It is not apparent that this argument can be generalized to apply to probability theories based on logics stronger than that of truth-functions. The argument does, however, provide a definite lower limit for the logics used in restrictions of reasonableness, for it shows that if such restrictions are to be non-redundant they must provide a finer analysis than that of the logic of truth-functions. Further, the argument suggests that such a finer analysis in addition to being necessary may also be sufficient, that restrictions on reasonableness of belief functions can be phrased simply by augmenting the base logic. To explore this suggestion let us look briefly at some specific ways in which logic, probability and belief are related.

One obvious way in which logic is related to belief is in the concept of transparency; the extent to which belief is invariant under logical transformations on the objects believed.[10] In the case of non-partial belief, this is the question of the nature of the class of transformations T such that for $t \in T$, belief in A implies belief in $t(A)$. When we generalize this question to apply to partial belief, we think first of defining transparency of partial belief under a transformation t as

$$p(A) \leqslant p(t(A))$$

(Thus, e.g., (iii) above is a case of this requirement where the transformation in question is simplification of conjunctions.)

But this is not sufficient, for in the case of partial belief transparency should apply as well to questions of dependence and independence. For example, if t is a synonymy transformation, then in order for belief to be transparent under t we should require not only that

$$p(A) = p(t(A))$$

but also that for each B

$$p(A \wedge B) = p((t(A)) \wedge B)$$
$$p_B(A) = p_B(t(A))$$

and so on.

Each set T of transformations determines in an obvious way a concept of synonymy, and in general what we require in order for a belief function p to be transparent under the set T is that the values of p remain invariant under replacement of synonyms in its arguments.

If we suppose that p is a truth-functional probability measure, i.e. that (i) and (ii) above are satisfied, then for T which include at least all tautological transformations the above general requirement has as a consequence that

(vii) If A is necessary by T then $p(A)=1$

(viii) If A and B are necessarily exclusive by T then $p(A \vee B)=p(A)+p(B)$.

Further in this case (vii) and (viii) are sufficient to provide for invariance under replacement of T-synonyms. Thus the laws of probability when relativized to a logic provide also an explication of transparency of partial belief.

Probabilistic theories of belief make important use of the concept of coherence, and it will be helpful to see how transparency and relativity to a logic are involved in this concept.

We can look at a set of bets as being given by a real-valued function p which assigns to each proposition in a set X a real number. Take it that an agent will put up $p(A)$ to receive 1 unit if A obtains. In such a case the agent puts up

$$\sum_{A \in X} p(A)$$

which we call the *cost* of X. Now should the set Y of propositions conjunctively occur, the agent receives 1 unit for each A in X implied by Y. Thus in this simplified case coherence can be described by the following condition:[11] C1 p is a coherent betting function on X just in case for each $X' \subseteq X$, there is some conjunctively consistent Y such that the cost of X' (computed according to p) is no greater than the number of propositions in X' implied by Y.

This description of coherence makes explicit its dependence upon logic, in particular upon the concepts of consistency and implication, and it is easy to see how a set of bets could be coherent with respect to one logic and not coherent with respect to another. We can now see how

Ramsey was not quite clear on the implications of his own theory: He took it to be an advantage of his view that with it one can dispense with the principle of indifference,[12] since it does not require that probabilities be uniquely determined. His remarks indicate first that he took this to be an advantage over the classical theories, and second that he thought he had also dispensed with relativity to logic.[13] Neither of these is the case. Ramsey's theory does require a characterization of *possible cases* in the form of a characterization of the consistent sets Y and their deductive closures. His relinquishment of the principle of indifference means simply that every normal mixing of these possible cases is a probability measure, such measures not being restricted to those in which the mixture is uniform. Thus the issue of the principle of indifference is for both Ramsey's and the classical theories, decided by whether one wants probabilities to be uniquely determined or not. Both accounts depend upon a characterization of possible cases. Given such a characterization the classical theories uniquely determine probabilities while Ramsey's does not. Either theory can be modified to match the other in this respect, and in particular the principle of indifference can be dropped from the classical theories to permit different weightings over models and extensions. The real and important difference between Ramsey's and the classical theories is that it relates probabilities to action: In La Place's theory probability is a metaphysical concept, and in Hume's it is mentalistic.

I have tried so far to show how the concepts of belief, reasonableness, and probability are related to logic. The weakest useful logic for these purposes is, I think, intuitionistic propositional logic. I have used the classical propositional logic above to simplify exposition, but the discussion could have been carried on, at the expense of some complication, in terms of the weaker logic. In particular the characterization of coherence is applicable in these terms. The strongest consistent logic is, of course, the logic of truth. In this logic, truth, validity, and consistency are not distinguished, and implication collapses to the material conditional. There is only one probability measure based on this logic, namely the two-valued measure which assigns 1 to every true proposition and 0 to every false proposition.

Between these two extremes are all consistent logics. Many of these are of little or no epistemological interest, but many others provide different and interesting concepts of belief, and accordingly of probability and coherence.

Suppose, for example, that we identify comprehension of a concept with knowledge of a function which generates the extension of the concept. We might call those concepts *absolutely comprehensible* which are *a priori* understood by everyone, and define comprehensibility relative to given concepts in an analogous way. It is a simple minded but not implausible extension of Church's thesis[14] to identify comprehensibility with general recursiveness. Then in view of the association of general recursiveness with intuitionistic arithmetic,[15] intuitionistic principles would assume some importance as epistemic principles. Definitions of comprehensible concepts would take on the status of axioms governing epistemic concepts, and every agent's beliefs would be transparent under (at least) the transformations of intuitionistic number theory. Thus in particular the theory of probability based on intuitionistic arithmetic would be a plausible logic of partial belief.

Some other examples of logics which may prove interesting as logics of partial belief in this way are free logics,[16] since they provide modes of inference which are valid in empty domains and thus permit inferences about other's beliefs without supposing that there is no disagreement about the existence of objects. Of course logics such as those put forward by Hintikka[17] which are explicitly epistemic would also provide the foundations for interesting theories of partial belief.

It seems to me to be a mistake to think of these and other logics as competing for the correct account of belief. Patrick Suppes remarked several years ago that there is probably no unique correct account of rationality,[18] he likened the concept of rationality in this respect to that of set, and I am inclined to think that this is also true of the concept of belief (and of desire as well).

II. A GENERAL FRAMEWORK

To make explicit the relations among belief, probability, reasonableness and coherence, it will be useful to have a general framework in which we can express relativity to a logic. Whenever we apply the laws of probability to judgments or propositions, we find in those laws references to logical concepts such as negation and disjunction, which may differ from logic to logic. Thus in providing a general framework we should try to express the laws of probability in a general way which depends only minimally upon such idiosyncratic concepts.

To do this we suppose that every logic when interpreted as relating sets of propositions yields a notion of implication which obeys the following laws.

(Reflexivity) If X is not null then X implies X.
(Expansion) If X implies Y, and X and Y are respectively subsets of X' and Y', then X' implies Y'.
(Transitivity) If X implies each A in Y (i.e. implies the unit set of A for each A in Y) and Y implies Z, then X implies Z.

Gaifman, and Scott and Krauss[19] make use of infinite formulas in relating logic to probability, for they restrict consideration to standard classical interpretations of the connectives. In order to eliminate reference to particular connectives here we use the device of sets of formulas instead. Given ordinary notions of conjunction and disjunction, implication as restricted above is conjunctive on the left and disjunctive on the right: X implies Y means that the truth of everything in X guarantees the truth of something in Y.

We can define in terms of implication some standard notions which are easily seen to be adequate in standard cases:

Every set which does not imply the null set is *consistent*.

A *valid* set is one which is implied by the null set.

A *conjunctively valid* set is one every member of which is valid.

A set X is *logically independendent* if no subset of X implies any other subset of X from which it is disjoint.

In general we shall consider collections P of propositions for which we have families $\{P_i\}$ of subsets obeying the following laws:

(i) Each P_i is consistent and non-null.
(ii) Each P_i is deductively closed in the sense that if X is implied by P_i then X and P_i are not disjoint.
(iii) The union of distinct P_i is always inconsistent.
(iv) The union of the family $\{P_i\}$ is the collection P.

We call such a collection of subsets of a set P a (finite or denumberable) *proper covering* of P.

In terms of probability theory, each P_i is a possible case. The principle of indifference would give the probability of a proposition in such a collection as the proportion of the P_i to which it belonged. Generalizing this is easy: any normal weighting of the P_i will give a probability measure.

Given a proper covering $\{P_i\}$ of a collection P, we define a *two valued disjunctive measure* p_i on subsets of P, to be a function which assigns 1 to each subset of P which intersects P_i and 0 to every other subset of P. By a *two valued conjunctive measure* p_i^* we mean a function which assigns 1 to every subset of P_i and 0 to every other subset of P. If p_i and p_i^* are two valued disjunctive and conjunctive measures respectively, they will have the following characteristics:[20]

$$p_i(\emptyset) = 0 = p_i^*(P)$$
$$p_i(P) = 1 = p_i^*(\emptyset)$$
$$p_i(A) = p_i^*(A) \quad (\text{For } A \in P)$$

If X is a denumerable subset of P then

II.1 $$p_i(X) = \sup_j p_i(X_j);\ X_j \text{ a finite subset of } X$$

II.2 $$p_i^*(X) = \inf_i p_i^*(X_j);\ X_j \text{ a finite subset of } X$$

Abandoning the principle of indifference means introducing weighting functions over the p_i and p_i^*. If $\{P_i\}$ is a proper covering of the collection P, then a *weighting function* w, is just a normal, non-negative weighting of the P_i, and hence of the p_i and p_i^*. I.e.

$$w(i) \geqslant 0 \text{ for each } i$$

and

$$\sum_i w(i) = 1$$

Each such w gives *disjunctive* and *conjunctive probability measures* defined on subsets of P: For X a subset of P

$$p(X) = \sum_i w(i) \cdot p_i(X)$$
$$p^*(X) = \sum_i w(i)\, p_i^*(X)$$

Measures defined in this way can be seen to obey the usual probabilistic laws in the following sense.

If X is valid then $p(X)=1$
If X is conjunctively valid then $p^*(X)=1$
If X implies Y then $p^*(X) \leqslant p(Y)$
If X is pairwise inconsistent then $p(X) = \sum_{A \in X} p(A)$

And we can define two senses of independence:

X is *weakly independent* in p (and p^*) if
$p^*(X) = \prod_{A \in X} p^*(A)$

X is *thoroughly independent* in p if every subset of X is weakly independent in p.

If $p^*(X) \neq 0$, we define

$$p_X(Y) = \frac{\sum_i (w(i) \cdot p_i^*(X) \cdot p_i(Y))}{p^*(X)}$$

$$p_X^*(Y) = \frac{\sum_i (w(i) \cdot p_i^*(X \cup Y))}{p^*(X)}$$

And we have the usual conditional characteristics:

If X implies Y then $p_X(Y)=1$
If X implies each A in Y then $p_X^*(Y)=1$
$p_X^*(Y)\, p^*(X) = p^*(X \cup Y)$
If $\{A, B\}$ is independent then (and only then)
$p_A^*(B) = p^*(B)$

EXAMPLE: Bernoulli sequences.
To illustrate the application of this framework in a particular case we can examine the logical bases of Bernoulli sequences. Let us make use of classical predicate logic with identity. We can in this logic characterize a denumerable class

$$N = \{n_0, n_1, \ldots\}$$

of distinct objects and a finite class (for given k)

$$K = \{a_1, \ldots, a_k\}$$

of objects distinct from each other and from the n_i. Further we can identify f as a (single-valued) one-place function from N to K. For simplicity we take there to be two classes of variables, one, $\{x_1, \ldots\}$ to range over N and the other $\{y_1, \ldots\}$ to range over K.

Now suppose our base logic to include these restrictions: i.e. suppose it to be essentially a classical first-order function theory with identity.

By a *diagram* we mean a complete set of functional equations, giving for each $n \in N$ a unique $f(n) \in K$. Each such diagram is a model. For closed sentences of the above theory we can define truth in a diagram M;

If A is a prime sentence, then A is of the form $f(n) = a$, and A is *true in* M just in case $A \in M$.

If A is $\exists x B(x)$ $(\forall x B(x))$ then A is *true in* M just in case for some (every) $n \in N$, $B(n)$ is true in M.

Similarly for $\exists y B(y)$ and $\forall y B(y)$, with range restricted to K.

And suppose the truth functions to be treated in the usual classical fashion.

Implication can be defined to hold between two sets just in case if every member of the first set is true in a diagram M then some member of the second set is true in M for every M. Implication then conforms to the laws given at the beginning of this section. Each diagram is conjunctively consistent. We can take P to include all consistent propositions on the given vocabulary, and for each diagram M_i we can take P_i to be the class of all sentences on the vocabulary which are true in M_i. Then the P_i form a proper cover of P.

We say in such a case that P forms a *Bernoullian class of index* K. Given such a class there is just one Bernoullian measure p (i.e. one pair, p and p^*) defined on the class, namely

(v) Every diagram is thoroughly independent in p.
(vi) For each $n \in N$ and $a \in K$, $p(f(n) = a) = 1/k$

We can thus see that Bernoulli sequences can be characterized in classical function theory with identity. The important notions are those of classical logic and those of thorough independence and the principle of indifference.

III. SOME APPLICATIONS OF THIS FRAMEWORK

The way in which the laws of probability are formulated in the preceding section is a straightforward generalization of the classical definition to permit weighting functions other than that in which all $w(i)$ are equal. The P_i are possible cases and every pair p_i, p_i^* describes a possible case as actual; $p_i(X)=1$ if some $A \in X$ holds in case P_i and $p_i^*(X)=1$ if all $A \in X$ hold in case P_i.

An important characteristic of these measures is given in the generalization of II.1 and II.2 to all measures p and p^*, under the restriction to the availability of finite proper coverings.

Let $\{P_i\}$ be a finite proper covering of P and X a denumerable subset of P. Then

III.1 $\quad p(X) = \sup_j p(X_j)$; X_j a finite subset of P

III.2 $\quad p^*(X) = \inf_j p^*(X_j)$; X_j a finite subset of P.

Proof of III.1

Clearly $\sup_j p(X_j) \leqslant p(X)$. To see the inequality in the other direction let X_j range over finite subsets of X and notice that

$$p(X) = \sum_i w(i) \cdot p_i(X)$$

so by II.1

$$p(X) = \sum_i w(i) \cdot \sup_j p_i(X_j)$$

Recalling that for each i, $\sup_j p_i(X_j) = 0$ if $X_j \cap P_i = \emptyset$
$= 1$ if $X_j \cap P_i \neq \emptyset$

we can suppose that for each i, there is a finite subset X_i of X such that

$$p_i(X_i) = \sup_j p_i(X_j)$$

and thus

$$p(X) = \sum_i w(i) \cdot p_i(X_i)$$

Now let $\bar{X} = \bigcup \{X_i\}$. Since $\{P_i\}$ is finite, $\bar{X}$ is finite and

$$p(\bar{X}) \leqslant \sup_j p(X_j)$$

Further, since each $\bar{X}_i \subseteq \bar{X}$, for each i

$$p_i(X_i) \leqslant p_i(\bar{X})$$

and hence

$$\sum_i w(i) \cdot p_i(X_i) \leqslant \sum_i w(i) \cdot p_i(\bar{X})$$

so that

$$p(X) \leqslant p(\bar{X}) \leqslant \sup_j p(X_j)$$

The proof of III.2 is similar.

This framework also provides a simple way to develop the coherence results in a generalized way. To illustrate this we show that if a betting function p is a probability measure, then p is coherent. In view of the condition C1 it will be sufficient to show that [21]

III.3 If p is a (disjunctive) probability measure based on a logic and defined on a set P for which there is a proper cover, then if $X \subseteq P$, X has a consistent (in terms of the same logic) subset which is at least as large as $\sum_{A \in X} p(A)$.

To see this suppose p and P as restricted in III.3, let $X \subseteq P$. Then for each $A \in X$, $p(A)$ is a weighted average of the two-valued disjunctive measures on A;

$$p(A) = \sum_i w(i) \cdot p_i(A)$$

and thus

$$\sum_{A \in X} p(A) = \sum_{A \in X} \sum_i w(i) \cdot p_i(A)$$
$$= \sum_i w(i) \cdot \sum_{A \in X} p_i(A)$$

Thus, since $0 \leqslant w(i) \leqslant 1$, we have that for some i

$$\sum_{A \in X} p(A) \leqslant \sum_{A \in X} p_i(A)$$

Further,

$$\{A \in X / p_i(A) = 1\} = X \cap P_i$$

and since P_i is conjunctively consistent, this set is also consistent.

III.3 expresses a useful boundary condition on probability sums, and makes explicit the relation of probability and consistency. It also helps in considering resolutions of what Henry Kyburg has described as the *lottery paradox*:[22] For any $\varepsilon > 0$, there are sets of propositions each of which has probability greater than $1 - \varepsilon$ and which are conjunctively inconsistent (probability and consistency being relative to the same logic). Thus we cannot plausibly define acceptability of a proposition in terms of high probability less than 1, unless we abandon the closure of acceptable propositions under conjunction. In a fair lottery of k tickets the chance that a given ticket will not win is $1 - 1/k$. For sufficiently high k we would thus (presumably) accept that a given ticket will not win. But this reasoning can be applied to each ticket in the lottery, and we would thus accept that no ticket will win, which is inconsistent.

This sort of argument shows that truth cannot be considered as a limit case of probability, and that the relation of probability to independence is not merely a generalization of the relation of truth to consistency.

The other side of the situation is described by III.3: Although for any $\varepsilon > 0$ there are conjunctively inconsistent sets of propositions each of which has probability greater than $1 - \varepsilon$, decreasing ε means that we increase the size of a largest consistent subset of the inconsistent set. In the lottery described above we are assured that a consistent subset of size $k - 1$ exists. Further, III.3 shows that each set of size $k - 1$ has a consistent subset of size at least

$$(k - 1)(1 - 1/k) = k - 2 + 1/k$$

i.e., that each subset of size $k - 1$ is consistent.

We can now say something about how probability measures function over propositions including logical connectives and operators. We restrict consideration here to logics in which conjunction, disjunction and conditionality are treated in the customary fashion. We suppose also that negation conforms to the rules:

If X, A implies B and X, A implies $\neg B$ then X implies $\neg A$
A, $\neg A$ implies $\emptyset$

And we say that negation is classical if

$\neg\neg A$ implies A

Under these restrictions, where X is a finite subset of P, (supposing P to be properly covered and p and p^* to be defined accordingly)

(i) $p^*(X)=p^*(\bigwedge X)$
(ii) $p(X)\leqslant p(\bigvee X)$
(iii) $p(A)+p(\neg A)\leqslant 1$
(iv) $p(A(a))\geqslant p(\forall x A(x))$
(v) $p(A(a))\leqslant p(\exists x A(x))$
(vi) $p^*(\{A, \neg A\})=0$
(vii) $p^*(\{A\rightarrow B, A\})\leqslant p^*(B)$
(viii) If X implies A then $p^*(\bigwedge X\rightarrow A)=1$
(ix) If $\neg$ is classical $p(A\vee\neg A)=1$

If the P_i are complete with respect to negation, so that for each i and each $A\in P$ at least one of $A,\neg A$ is in P_i, then

(x) $p(A)+p(\neg A)=1=p(\{A, \neg A\})$
(xi) $p(X)=p(\bigvee X)$

In this case measures on P will have all the characteristics of classical measures. (I.e. of measures in which $\neg$ is classical.) Thus restriction to P_i which are complete in the above sense is stronger than restriction to logics with classical negation, since neither (x) nor (xi) hold in general in the latter.

Let us say that the P_i are *complete with respect to the individuals D* if

$$\forall x A(x)\in P_i;\Leftrightarrow \underset{\in D}{\forall a},\ A(a)\in P_i$$

and

$$\exists x A(x)\in P_i;\Leftrightarrow \underset{\in D}{\exists a},\ A(a)\in P_i$$

for each P_i.

Then if $\{P_i\}$ is complete with respect to D,

$$p^*(\forall x A(x))=p^*(\{A(a)\mid a\in D\})$$
$$p(\exists x A(x))=p(\{A(a)\mid a\in D\})$$

And by III.1, III.2, if $\{P_i\}$ is finite $p^*(\forall x A(x))=\inf_j p^*(X_j)$ (X_j finite $\subseteq\{A(a)\mid a\in D\}$) $p(\exists x A(x))=\sup_j p(X_j)$ (X_j finite $\subseteq\{A(a)\mid a\in D\}$)

The possible worlds of a modal logic form in some cases a proper covering $\{P_i\}$.[23] In the simplest case the base logic will be S_5, and there will be some subclass N of $\bigcap \{P_i\}$ such that

$$\Box A \in \bigcap \{P_i\} \Leftrightarrow A \in N$$

In this case every probability measure will be two-valued on formulas of the form $\Box A$, and we shall have for example

$$p(\Box A) \leqslant p(A)$$
$$p(A \wedge \Box B) = p(A) \cdot p(\Box B)$$
$$p(A \vee \Box B) = \max [p(A), p(\Box B)]$$
$$p(\forall x \Box B) = p(\Box \forall x B)$$

and so on. In general in such structures for every measure p

$$\Box A \in P_i, \text{ for some } i \Rightarrow p(A) = 1$$

And if $N = \bigcap \{P_i\}$, the distinction between necessity and maximal probability collapses in the following sense

$$p(A) = 1 \text{ for all } p \Rightarrow p(\Box A) = 1 \text{ for all } p$$

Probability based on S_5 provides a plausible logic of acceptance, interpreting acceptance of A as $p(\Box A) = 1$ (and rejection of A as $p(\Box \neg A) = 1$). Given P, $\{P_i\}$ and N, we can distinguish the following classes of propositions.

Logical truths $= \{A \mid A \text{ is valid}\}$
Accepted propositions $= \{A \mid p(\Box A) = 1\} = \{A \mid \forall p, p(\Box A) = 1\}$
Universally maximally probable propositions $= \{A \mid \forall p, p(A) = 1\}$
Maximally probable propositions in the measure p $= \{A \mid p(A) = 1\}$

Probability based in this way does not allow assignments other than 0 and 1 to propositions of the form $\Box A$. To do that we need weaker modal systems such as S_4 in which $\Box A$ may hold in some world even when A fails to hold in some world.

REFERENCES

* I am indebted to Patrick Suppes for several conversations which helped clarify many of the questions with which this paper is concerned. Work on this paper was supported in part by NSF Grant #Gs-2099.

[1] Second edition, Chicago, 1962.
[2] P. S. La Place, *A Philosophical Essay On Probabilities*, New York 1951. D. Hume, *A Treatise of Human Nature* (ed. by L. A. Selby-Bigge), Oxford 1888, esp. Sections 11 and 13 of Book I Part III.
[3] Cf. e. g. Hume's discussion, *op. cit.*, pp. 128f.
[4] As evidenced in his 'The Aim of Inductive Logic' in *Logic, Methodology and Philosophy of Science* (ed. by E. Nagel, P. Suppes and A. Tarski), Stanford 1962.
[5] F. P. Ramsey, 'Truth and Probability' in *The Foundations of Mathematics*, London 1931. B. De Finetti, 'La prevision, ses lois logiques, ses sources subjectives', *Annales de L'Institut Henri Poincaré*, **7** (1937).
[6] For a guide to the considerable literature on this subject see the introduction to H. Kyburg, and H. Smokler, *Studies in Subjective Probability*, New York 1964. This book includes Ramsey's article mentioned above as well as a translation of De Finetti's monograph.
[7] Cf. my article 'Some Remarks on Coherence and Subjective Probability', *Philosophy of Science*, **32** (January 1965) 4, where this is done rather clumsily.
[8] 'The Aim of Inductive Logic.'
[9] The situation remains as far as I know as it was described by Carnap in 'On the Application of Inductive Logic', *Philosophy and Phenomenological Research*, **8** (September, 1947), 133–148. Cf. R. C. Jeffrey, 'Goodman's Query', *Journal of Philosophy* **63** (May 26, 1966) **11**, 281–288 for a proposal and my article 'Characteristics of Projectible Predicates', *Journal of Philosophy*, **64** (May, 1967), 280–286 in which the proposal is shown to be inadequate.
[10] In 'Judgment and Belief', in *The Logical Way of Doing Things* (ed. by K. Lambert), New York, 1969, I associate degree of transparency of belief with the extent to which it is behavioristic as distinct from mentalistic. That paper is concerned with the relation between mentalistic and behavioristic belief, and ignores – except for a few casual comments – the question of the nature of the theory of probability associated with this view of belief. Both there and in the present essay belief is taken to be relative to a logic, and both papers are attempts at accounting for features of this relativity.
[11] The full condition is: p is a coherent betting function on X just in case for every pair X_1, X_2 of disjoint subsets of X, there is some conjunctively consistent Y such that Y implies n_1 propositions in X_1, n_2 propositions in X_2 and

$$(n_1 - \sum_{A \in X_2} p(A)) \geqslant (n_2 - \sum_{A \in X_1} p(A)).$$

We think of the agent betting on propositions in X_1 and against those in X_2. C_1 is a special case of this.
[12] 'Truth and Probability', p. 189.
[13] He does say that probability is a generalization of formal logic (*ibid.*, p. 186) but he does not appear to think of different probability theories as based upon different logics.
[14] *Church's Thesis* is that all and only general recursive functions are effectively computable. It was first proposed by Alonzo Church in 'An Unsolvable Problem of Elementary Number Theory', *American Journal of Mathematics* **58** (1936) 345–363. Cf. S. C. Kleene's discussion in *Introduction to Metamathematics*, Princeton 1952, p. 130 ff.
[15] See S. C. Kleene and R. E. Vesley, *The Foundations of Intuitionistic Mathematics*, Amsterdam 1965.
[16] See, for example, B. van Fraassen, 'Singular Terms, Truth Value Gaps, and Free Logic', *Journal of Philosophy* **63** (1966) 481–495.

[17] In, for example, *Knowledge and Belief*, Cornell 1962.
[18] P. Suppes, 'The Philosophical Relevance of Decision Theory', *Journal of Philosophy* **58** (1961) 605–614.
[19] H. Gaifman, 'Concerning Measures on First Order Calculi', *Israel Journal of Mathematics* **2**, 1–18. D. Scott and P. Krauss, 'Assigning Probabilities to Logical Formulas', in *Aspects of Inductive Logic* (ed. by J. Hintikka and P. Suppes), Amsterdam 1966, pp. 219–264.
[20] I use $A, B, C, \ldots$ to range over propositions, $X, Y, Z, \ldots$ and $P, Q, \ldots$ to range over sets of propositions. P always refers to a set of propositions which is properly covered by the family $\{P_i\}$. In referring to the unit set $\{A\}$, set brackets are frequently omitted.
[21] Cf. reference 11 for the generalized form. The proof does not differ essentially.
[22] Cf. e.g. *Probability and the Logic of Rational Belief*, Middletown 1961.
[23] In R. C. Stalnaker, 'Probability and Conditionals', mimeographed, Yale Univ., this relation is explored in some depth.

PETER W. WOODRUFF

LOGIC AND TRUTH VALUE GAPS*

A salient feature of contemporary philosophical logic is the great interest in so-called 'free logics', logics admitting non-denoting terms without paraphrase. Proponents of such logics have generally followed one of two approaches, each of which was considered and rejected by Russell in 'On Denoting'. The first, suggested by Meinong, requires the introduction of possible but non-existent objects as 'references' for non-denoting terms. This approach has been by far the more popular among contemporary free logicians, perhaps because many of them came to free logic by way of modal logic.[1] The second approach was first suggested by Frege[2] and later developed at length by Strawson.[3] Roughly put, it characterizes sentences containing non-denoting terms as truth-valueless, i.e. as neither true nor false, while at the same time insisting that such sentences are meaningful and express (truth-valueless) propositions.

Despite its philosophical merit, Strawson's approach has found few adherents among formal logicians. The principal reason for this situation seems to be a recognition that this approach requires some sort of 'three-valued' logic, combined with a belief that such a logic will necessarily be either unintuitive or impractical or both. These sentiments are aptly expressed by Scott in his contribution to the present volume:

> Yes, yes, I can hear the objections being shouted from all corners. If one is going to use undefined terms, why not undefined truth values? Isn't that more natural? Maybe so, but I have yet to see a really workable three-valued logic. I know it can be defined, and at least four times a year someone comes up with the idea anew, but it has *not* really been developed to the point where one could say it is pleasant to work with. Maybe the day will come, but I have yet to be convinced.

One possible response to this position is that of van Fraassen[4], who has developed a logic with truth value gaps which is essentially a modal extension of classical logic. In his *presuppositional languages* all theorems of two-valued logic are preserved (though not all metatheorems). In the present essay I shall meet Scott's challenge directly by constructing a

K. Lambert (ed.), Philosophical Problems in Logic.

system of three-valued propositional logic which (a) is 'really workable', (b) permits the formulation in the object language of non-trivial theories of truth and presupposition and (c) possesses a number of interesting extensions to a full first-order system, one of which is a truly Strawsonian free logic.[5]

I. TRUTH VALUE GAPS

In this section I shall discuss the heuristic considerations on which the present system is based; in particular, the choice of truth tables for the standard Boolean connectives. The system I arrive at is not really new[6], but my approach to its formalization is quite different. The fundamental new concept I introduce is a distinction between two types of assertion, the consequent application of which in semantics and proof theory enables me to overcome most of the usual objections to three-valued logic as voiced by Scott.

We wish to devise a logic which admits truth value gaps. On the usual understanding of logic as the theory of valid inference, this means that we wish to be able to evaluate inferences which involve sentences which may be neither true nor false. But the way in which inferences involve sentences is via assertions; i.e. an inference is a move from certain assertions to another assertion, and we use sentences to make the assertions. An inference will be valid if and only if whenever the premises are correct assertions the conclusion is also. We have therefore to determine what constitutes correctness of assertion when the sentence used to make the assertion may lack a truth value.

In the present context there are two distinct ways in which one may do this: one may either commit oneself to the truth of the proposition or merely to its non-falsity. The first mode of assertion I call *unconditional* or *strong*, the second *hedged* or *weak*. Clearly an unconditional assertion is correct if and only if the proposition asserted is true, and similarly for hedged assertion and non-falsity.

Let p and q be sentences and $p \vee q$ their disjunction. Then it is natural to require that the assertion that $p \vee q$ should be correct if either the assertion that p or the assertion that q is correct, where the assertions of the parts are taken in the same sense, weak or strong, as the assertion of the whole. This determines the following 'truth table' for disjunction:

p	q	$p \vee q$
t	t	t
t		t
t	f	t
	t	t
	f	
f	t	t
f		
f	f	f

Similar considerations lead to a table for conjunction which is the dual of that for disjunction.

For negation we need to distinguish two ways of denying a proposition; an unconditional denial is correct iff the proposition denied is false and a hedged denial iff it is not true. Then it is natural to require that if $\sim p$ is the negation of p, then its assertion should be correct, in either sense, just in case the denial of p is correct, in the same sense. This leads to the usual table for negation:

p	$\sim p$
t	f
f	t

There are numerous ways of defining an implication operator. For convenience we shall use the 'material implication' defined in the usual way in terms of negation and disjunction: $p \supset q = \sim p \vee q$. This connective has the following table:

p	q	$p \supset q$
t	t	t
t		
t	f	f
	t	t
	f	
f	t	t
f		t
f	f	t

Implication will be taken as primitive in the syntax of our system, the others mentioned above being defined in terms of it.

In addition to notions taken over from two-valued logic, we shall introduce as primitive two notions which are peculiar to a logic with gaps. The first is a one-place connective T, the *truth operator*.[7] Intuitively Tp is to read 'it is true that p'. T is to have the following table, which clearly reflects the intended interpretation:

p	Tp
t	**t**
	f
f	**f**

Finally, we introduce a constant truth-valueless sentence u which intuitively we may think of as a sentence such as 'the round square is red'. This constant serves to secure the functional completeness of our system and in conjunction with T and $\supset$ to permit the definition of negation.

II. MEANINGLESSNESS

Many proponents of a logic with gaps have proposed the following table for disjunction in place of that of the previous section[8]:

p	q	$p \vee q$
t	**t**	**t**
t		
t	**f**	**t**
	t	
	f	
f	**t**	**t**
f		
f	**f**	**f**

The leading idea here is that not having a truth value is tantamount to meaninglessness, and that if any part of a wff is meaningless then so is the whole wff.

I shall present in Section V a detailed argument in favor of my choice of tables as against that above. The fundamental theme of that argument will be that, as noted, Frege and Strawson intended lack of truth value to mean only lack of reference, not meaninglessness or lack of sense. In addition, of course, there is the direct justification of our tables offered in the previous section.

III. SYNTAX

I turn now to the construction of the system **U** of logic with truth value gaps. The present section defines the syntax of **U**, while subsequent sections will be devoted to semantic and deductive concepts.

A *morphology* **M** for **U** is a structure consisting of a non-empty well-ordered set $At_{\mathbf{M}}$ of *atomic formulas*, together with the improper symbols

$$\supset, T, (,)$$

and the primitive constant

$$u$$

The set $\mathbf{W_M}$ of (well-formed) *formulas* of **M** consists of u and the elements of At, as well as $(A \supset B)$ and TA whenever A and B are formulas. We use 'A', 'B' etc. as variables ranging over $\mathbf{W_M}$ and follow the notational conventions of Church.[9] We adopt the following symbolic definitions:

D1. $f = Tu$
D2. $\sim A = (A \supset f)$
D3. $(A \vee B) = (\sim A \supset B)$
D4. $(A \,\&\, B) = \sim(\sim A \vee \sim B)$
D5. $(A \equiv B) = ((A \supset B) \,\&\, (B \supset A))$
D6. $FA = T \sim A$
D7. $*A = \sim FA$
D8. $+A = (TA \vee FA)$
D9. $(A \rightarrow B) = (TA \supset TB)$
D10. $(A \Rightarrow B) = (+A \rightarrow B)$
D11. $(A \cong B) = ((TA \equiv TB) \,\&\, (*A \equiv *B))$

We read 'F...' as 'it is false that...', '...$\rightarrow$---' as 'that...implies that---', '...$\Rightarrow$---' as 'that...presupposes that---' and the other connectives either in the usual way or in accordance with their definitions and the above readings.

We need to make one further stipulation which is not, strictly speaking, part of the syntax of **U**. Our basic semantic and deductive concepts will be defined below not directly for formulas of a morphology **M** but rather, in line with the discussion of the previous section, for assertions made by using these formulas. We therefore need some way of referring to assertions, and we provide this as follows: a formula standing alone represents the unconditional assertion of the formula; an underlined wff represents the hedged assertion of the formula. Thus if A and B are formulas,

$$A \supset B$$

stands for the unconditional assertion of the *formula* $A \supset B$, and

$$\underline{A \supset B}$$

for its hedged assertion. The use of these notations will become clearer when we apply them in subsequent sections. If A is a formula, then '(A)' will be used ambiguously to denote either kind of assertion made with the use of A, subject to the convention that in a given context it is to stand for the same kind of assertion throughout.

IV. SEMANTICS

The main outlines of the semantics of **U** were indicated in Section II. We depart slightly from our position there in that for convenience we shall fill truth value gaps with a third 'value' **u**, so that a value will be defined for every wff by a given interpretation. This does not, however, change the principal interpretation of **U**, for we shall think of 'having the value **u**' as equivalent in meaning to 'being undefined' or 'not having value **t** or **f**.'

An *interpretation* **I** of a morphology **M** for **U** is a function which assigns to each element of $\mathbf{W_M}$ a value in $\{\mathbf{t}, \mathbf{u}, \mathbf{f}\}$ subject to the following conditions:

(Si) $\mathbf{I}(A \supset B) = \mathbf{t}$ iff $\mathbf{I}(A) = \mathbf{f}$ or $\mathbf{I}(B) = \mathbf{t}$; $\mathbf{I}(A \supset B) = \mathbf{f}$ iff $\mathbf{I}(A) = \mathbf{t}$ and $\mathbf{I}(B) = \mathbf{f}$.

(Sii) $\mathbf{I}(TA) = \mathbf{t}$ iff $\mathbf{I}(A) = \mathbf{t}$; otherwise, $\mathbf{I}(TA) = \mathbf{f}$.

(Siii) $\mathbf{I}(u) = \mathbf{u}$

These conditions and those thereby induced for the defined connectives are summarized in the following tables:[10]

u	f
u	**f**

A	$\sim A$	TA	FA	$*A$	$+A$
t	f	t	f	t	t
u	u	f	f	t	f
f	t	f	t	f	t

A	B	$A \supset B$	$A \vee B$	$A \& B$	$A \equiv B$	$A \to B$	$A \Rightarrow B$	$A \cong B$
t	t	t	t	t	t	t	t	t
t	u	u	t	u	u	f	f	f
t	f	f	t	f	f	f	f	f
u	t	t	t	u	u	t	t	f
u	u	u	u	u	u	t	t	t
u	f	u	u	f	u	t	t	f
f	t	t	t	f	f	t	t	f
f	u	t	u	f	u	t	f	f
f	f	t	f	f	t	t	f	t

An assertion A is *correct* on interpretation **I** iff $\mathbf{I}(A)=\mathbf{t}$; $\underline{A}$ is correct iff $\mathbf{I}(A)\neq\mathbf{f}$. If Γ is a set of assertions, then the inference from Γ to (A) is *valid* ($\Gamma \vDash (A)$) iff (A) is correct on every interpretation on which every member of Γ is correct. For example:

$$\{A, \underline{A \supset B}\} \vDash \underline{B}.$$

An assertion is *valid* iff validly inferred from the empty set.

Let a formula be called *classical* if it is built up from atomic formulas using only $\sim$, $\supset$, $\vee$, & and $\equiv$. It follows from our definitions that no unconditional assertion of a classical formula is valid, and that the hedged assertion of a classical formula is valid iff the formula is a theorem of two-valued logic. In this limited sense **U** contains all of two-valued logic. Let a formula constructed from atoms using only $\to$ be called '$\to$-pure'. Then the assertion (of either sort) of an $\to$-pure formula will be valid iff it is a theorem of pure classical implication.

V. TRUTH VALUE GAPS AGAIN

In Section II we indicated that some have used the following weak tables for the classical connectives:

A	$\sim A$
t	f
u	u
f	t

A	B	$A \supset B$	$A \vee B$	$A \& B$	$A \equiv B$
t	t	t	t	t	t
t	u	u	u	u	u
t	f	f	t	f	f
u	t	u	u	u	u
u	u	u	u	u	u
u	f	u	u	u	u
f	t	t	t	f	f
f	u	u	u	u	u
f	f	t	f	f	t

It might be urged that these are the correct tables given the present motivation, on the grounds that the reference of the whole is to be determined by the reference of the parts, and hence that if any part fails to refer, so must the whole. This would not, it is argued, conflict with the idea that referenceless sentences may yet have senses, for the sense of the whole is to be determined by the sense of the parts, not by their reference.

This argument is plausible, but overlooks the fact that the Frege-Strawson theory makes a close connection between sense and reference. Frege speaks of expressions as referring *via* their senses[11], and Strawson occasionally identifies senses with 'rules for referring'.[12] One way of making this concrete is to identify the sense of an expression e with the function which assigns to any possible world the reference of e in that world. If in the present context we identify possible worlds with interpretations, then we can offer the following argument against the weak interpretation:

(A) It is generally recognized that the set of propositions expressible in known languages has at least the structure of a lattice, if we take the meet of the proposition that p and the proposition that q to be the proposition that p and q, and their join to be the proposition that p or q.[13]

(B) The preceding discussion suggests that we define the proposition $[A]$ expressed by a formula A as a function whose value for an interpretation is the value of the interpretation for that wff:

$$[A](\mathbf{I}) = \mathbf{I}(A) \quad \text{for every interpretation } \mathbf{I}.$$

Furthermore, according to Paragraph (A) we should have

$$[A] \wedge [B] = [A \& B]$$

and

$$[A] \vee [B] = [A \vee B].$$

Finally, the set of propositions should be a lattice with respect to $\wedge$ and $\vee$.

(C) If we take as our set of interpretations those defined in the previous section, then the algebra of propositions indeed proves to have the structure of a lattice. The class of algebras obtained by defining operations corresponding to the other connectives, especially the non-classical ones, turns out to be quite interesting, and has been extensively studied under the rubric 'Łukasiewiczian algebra'.[14]

(D) If, on the other hand, we define our interpretations in accordance with the weak tables of the present section, then in general we obtain at best a trivial (one-element) lattice. For we would have for any proposition $[A]$

$$[A] \wedge [u] = [u] = [A] \vee [u]$$

but in a lattice this implies that $[A]=[u]$. Thus we should have at most one proposition and hence also $\mathbf{t}=\mathbf{f}=\mathbf{u}$.

It appears then that for a theory of truth value gaps according to which expressions may have (non-trivial) sense without reference, the strong senses we have given to the connectives are to be preferred.[15]

VI. PROOF THEORY

We must now provide a deductive codification of the valid inferences of **U**. Our principle aim will be to devise a natural deduction system in which there are no axioms but only introduction and elimination rules which characterize the various connectives in terms of their logical behavior. This system will be called **NU**.

Since our notion of valid inference applies to assertions, our deductive notions will do likewise. Our proofs will thus contain (among other things) both plain and underlined formulas, the former representing strong and the latter weak assertions. In other details, including typographical style, we follow Fitch.[16]

A *proof of depth n* in **NU** is a finite sequence each element of which is either

(1) a premise,
(2) a proof of depth n', $n' < n$, or
(3) a consequence of previous items by one of the rules of direct consequence listed below.

We regard this definition as implicitly defining 'premise'; a premise is any element not justified by (2) or (3). A *proof* is any proof of finite depth.

The rules of direct consequence which we are about to state are designed to provide for the introduction into discourse and use therein of the various connectives. Since we have two kinds of assertion in our discourse, we shall have to provide for the introduction and elimination of connectives in both kinds of context. With a few exceptions the rules will be named by writing the connective involved followed by '**I**' (for introduction) or '**E**' (for elimination); if the rule concerns a hedged context the connective will be underlined. The exceptions are the rules **K**, $\supset$ **p** and $\underline{\supset}$ **p**. The first is a structural rule of weakening, named by analogy with the corresponding rule in a sequenzen-kalkül. The latter two correspond to the so-called 'Peirce's law' of classical implication and are also structural in the sense that if we modified the structure of our proofs slightly we could dispense with them.[17]

K	$\underline{A}$ is a direct consequence (d.c.) of A.
$\supset$ **I**	$A \supset B$ is a d.c. of assertions $(A_1), \ldots, (A_n)$ and a proof whose premises are $(A_1), \ldots, (A_n)$ and $\underline{A}$ and of which B is an element.
$\underline{\supset}$ **I**	$\underline{A \supset B}$ is a d.c. of assertions $(A_1), \ldots, (A_n)$ and a proof whose premises are $(A_1), \ldots, (A_n)$ and A and of which $\underline{B}$ is an element.
$\supset$ **E**	B is a d.c. of $\underline{A}$ and $A \supset B$.
$\underline{\supset}$ **E**	$\underline{B}$ is a d.c. of A and $\underline{A \supset B}$.
$\supset$ **p**	$\underline{A}$ is a d.c. of assertions $(A_1), \ldots, (A_n)$ and a proof whose premises are $(A_1), \ldots, (A_n)$ and $A \supset B$ and of which $\underline{A}$ is an element.
$\underline{\supset}$ **p**	A is a d.c. of assertions $(A_1), \ldots, (A_n)$ and a proof whose premises are $(A_1), \ldots, (A_n)$ and $\underline{A \supset B}$ and of which A is an element.
TI	TA is a d.c. of A.

$\underline{T}$**E** A is a d.c. of $\underline{TA}$.
$\underline{u}$**I** $\underline{u}$ is a d.c. of $\underline{A}$.
u**E** A is a d.c. of u.

A proof which occurs as an element of another is said to be *subordinate to* (a sub-proof of) that proof. If P' is a sub-proof of P, and (A) is a premise of P' which also occurs as an element of P before P', then we say that (A) is justified by *reiteration* (with respect to P). Evidently we can infer $A \supset B$ by $\supset I$ from a subproof every premise of which other than $\underline{A}$ is justified by reiteration and of which B is an element. Given this convention, the rules above may be stated schematically in the following manner (taking $\supset$**p** and $\underline{T}$**E** as examples):

$$\begin{array}{l|l} & \begin{array}{|l} A \supset B \\ \hline \cdot \\ \cdot \\ \cdot \\ \underline{A} \end{array} \\ & \underline{A} \end{array} \qquad \qquad \begin{array}{|l} \underline{TA} \\ \hline A \end{array}$$

In this manner we list some derived rules of consequence induced by our definitions:

$$\mathbf{*I}\ \begin{array}{|l} \underline{A} \\ \hline {*A} \end{array} \quad \underline{\mathbf{*}}\mathbf{E}\ \begin{array}{|l} \underline{*A} \\ \hline \underline{A} \end{array} \quad +I\ \begin{array}{|l} \begin{array}{|l} \underline{A} \\ \hline A \end{array} \\ +A \end{array} \quad \pm\mathbf{E}\ \begin{array}{|l} \underline{+A} \\ \underline{A} \\ \hline A \end{array}$$

$$\to\mathbf{I}\ \begin{array}{|l} \begin{array}{|l} A \\ \hline B \end{array} \\ A \to B \end{array} \quad \underline{\to}\mathbf{E}\ \begin{array}{|l} A \\ \underline{A \to B} \\ \hline B \end{array} \quad \Rightarrow\mathbf{I}\ \begin{array}{|l} \begin{array}{|l} A \\ \hline B \end{array} \\ \begin{array}{|l} \sim A \\ \hline B \end{array} \\ A \Rightarrow B \end{array} \quad \underline{\Rightarrow}\mathbf{E}\ \begin{array}{|l} A \\ \underline{A \Rightarrow B} \\ \hline B \end{array} \quad \begin{array}{|l} \sim A \\ \underline{A \Rightarrow B} \\ \hline B \end{array}$$

As an example of proof technique we present the derivation of $\underline{*}\mathbf{E}$:

(1)	$\underline{T(A \supset Tu) \supset Tu}$	P (cf D1, 2, 6 and 7)
(2)	$\quad \underline{A \supset Tu}$	P
(3)	$\quad T(A \supset Tu)$	(2), T**I**
(4)	$\quad \underline{T(A \supset Tu) \supset Tu}$	(1), Reiteration
(5)	$\quad \underline{Tu}$	(3), (4), $\supseteq$ **E**
(6)	$\quad u$	(5), $\underline{T}$**E**
(7)	$\quad A$	(6), u**E**
(8)	$\quad \underline{A}$	(7), **K**
(9)	$\underline{A}$	(2)–(8), $\supset$ **p**

If Γ is a set of assertions, and (A) an assertion, we say that (A) is *deducible from* Γ in **NU** ($\Gamma \vdash (A)$) iff there is a proof all of whose premises belong to Γ and of which (A) is an element. An assertion deducible from the empty set is a *theorem*. We shall show in the next section that the relation of deducibility in fact coincides with that of valid inference.

VII. COHERENCE: SEMANTIC CONSISTENCY AND COMPLETENESS

The consistency of **NU** with respect to the semantics of Section V is easily established by a double induction on the depth and length of proofs. Thus we have

THEOREM 1: If (A) is deducible from Γ then the inference from Γ to (A) is valid.

On the other hand, we sketch a proof of the semantic completeness of **NU**.

THEOREM 2: If the inference from Γ to (A) is valid then (A) is deducible from Γ.

PROOF: Let us call a set Δ of assertions (A)-*maximal* iff (a) not $\Delta \vdash (A)$ and (b) if Δ' is a proper superset of Δ, then $\Delta' \vdash (A)$. Then the proofs of the following lemmas are not substantially different from similar ones for two-valued logic.[18]

LEMMA 1: If not $\Gamma \vdash (A)$, then there is an (A)-maximal set Δ such that $\Gamma \subseteq \Delta$.

LEMMA 2: The following conditions hold of any (A)-maximal set Δ:

(i) $\Delta \vdash (B)$ iff $(B) \in \Delta$

(ii) $\Delta \cup \{(B)\} \vdash (A)$ iff $(B) \notin \Delta$

(iii) (a) $B \supset C \in \Delta$ iff either $\underline{B} \notin \Delta$ or $C \in \Delta$

(b) $\underline{B \supset C} \in \Delta$ iff either $B \notin \Delta$ or $\underline{C} \in \Delta$

(iv) (a) $TB \in \Delta$ if $B \in \Delta$

(b) $\underline{TB} \in \Delta$ only if $B \in \Delta$

(v) (a) $u \notin \Delta$

(b) $\underline{u} \in \Delta$

PROOF: We confine ourselves to (iii) (b). If $\underline{B \supset C} \in \Delta$ and $B \in \Delta$, then by $\supseteq E$ and (i) we have $\underline{C} \in \Delta$. On the other hand, if $\underline{C} \in \Delta$ then since $\underline{C} \vdash \underline{B \supset C}$ we have by (i) $\underline{B \supset C} \in \Delta$. Finally, if $B \notin \Delta$, then if also $\underline{B \supset C} \notin \Delta$ we must by (ii) have both $\Delta \cup \{B\} \vdash (A)$ and $\Delta \cup \{\underline{B \supset C}\} \vdash (A)$. Then the following proof sketch shows that $\Delta \vdash (A)$, contrary to hypothesis.

CASE 1: $(A) = A$

	$\mid\ \Delta$	P
(1)	$\mid\ \mid\ \underline{A \supset C}$	P
(2)	$\mid\ \mid\ \mid\ B$	P
(3)	$\mid\ \mid\ \mid\ A$	Δ, Reit., (2), by hyp.
(4)	$\mid\ \mid\ \mid\ \underline{A \supset C}$	(1), Reit.
(5)	$\mid\ \mid\ \mid\ \underline{C}$	(3), (4), $\supseteq$ **E**
(6)	$\mid\ \mid\ \underline{B \supset C}$	(2)–(5), $\supseteq$ **I**
(7)	$\mid\ \mid\ A$	Δ, Reit., (6), by hyp.
(8)	$\mid\ A$	(1)–(7), $\supseteq$ **p**

CASE 2: $(A) = \underline{A}$

	$\mid\ \Delta$	P
(1)	$\mid\ \mid\ A \supset C$	P
(2)	$\mid\ \mid\ \mid\ B$	P
(3)	$\mid\ \mid\ \mid\ \underline{A}$	Δ, Reit., (2), by hyp.
(4)	$\mid\ \mid\ \mid\ A \supset C$	(1), Reit.
(5)	$\mid\ \mid\ \mid\ C$	(3), (4), $\supset$ **E**
(6)	$\mid\ \mid\ \mid\ \underline{C}$	(5), **K**
(7)	$\mid\ \mid\ \underline{B \supset C}$	(2)–(5), $\supseteq$ **I**
(8)	$\mid\ \mid\ \underline{A}$	Δ, Reit., (7), by hyp.
(9)	$\mid\ \underline{A}$	(1)–(8), $\supset$ **p**

LEMMA 3: Let Δ be (A)-maximal, and let $\mathbf{I}_\Delta$ be defined as follows for each $B \in \mathbf{W}_\mathbf{M}$:

(i) $\mathbf{I}_\Delta(B) = \mathbf{t}$ iff $\underline{B} \in \Delta$
(ii) $\mathbf{I}_\Delta(B) = \mathbf{u}$ iff $\underline{B} \in \Delta$ but $B \notin \Delta$
(iii) $\mathbf{I}_\Delta(B) = \mathbf{f}$ iff $\underline{B} \notin \Delta$.

Then $\mathbf{I}_\Delta$ is an interpretation of $\mathbf{M}$ and hence for any subset Γ of Δ, not $\Gamma \models (A)$.

PROOF: By Lemma 2 and definitions.

Returning to the proof of Theorem 2, suppose that (A) is not deducible from Γ. Then by Lemma 1 there is an (A)-maximal set Δ which includes Γ. By Lemma 3, the inference from Γ to (A) is not valid. The theorem now follows by contraposition. **Q.E.D.**

VIII. TRUTH AND PRESUPPOSITION

Two important applications of our system are the elementary theories of truth and presupposition embodied, on the principal interpretation, in the connectives T and $\Rightarrow$. We call these theories elementary because they treat the two connectives as object language operators rather than as meta-linguistic predicates; we shall however argue that a certain 'meta-linguistic' flavor remains.

The first test which any purported theory of truth must meet is of course satisfaction of Tarski's Convention **T**.[19] The latter will however have to be modified, since it is intended to cover theories in which truth is represented by a metalinguistic predicate. Roughly speaking, we have to show that for any formula A of a morphology $\mathbf{M}$ for $\mathbf{U}$, the formulas A and TA are provably equivalent in $\mathbf{NU}$.

Unfortunately, there are a number of senses which may be given to 'provably equivalent' in the present context, and in some of these senses the condition is satisfied, in others not. Thus if

(1) A is provably equivalent with TA

means

(2) $\vdash A \cong TA$

then (1) must be false, for we have $\mathbf{I}(A \cong TA) = \mathbf{f}$ when $\mathbf{I}(A) = \mathbf{u}$. Now (2) will hold iff A and TA have exactly the same truth-table, and this in turn, by the considerations of Section V, will be the case iff A and TA express the same proposition, or 'have the same sense'. But many philosophers have denied that there is an identity of *sense* between e.g.

(3) Tom is tall

and

(4) It is true that Tom is tall,

principally on the grounds that the latter is in some sense metalinguistic while the former is not.[20] I shall argue shortly that the fact that (4) is false if (3) is truth-valueless is a reflection of this fact. For this reason I see the failure of (2) not as a refutation of the present theory of truth, but rather as a vindication of the above-mentioned philosophers.

If we admit that (3) and (4) have in general different senses, it is nevertheless clear that there is a close connection between their truth conditions; indeed, given our semantics the one will be true if and only if the other is. In fact, we have both

(5) $TA \vdash A$

and

(6) $A \vdash TA$;

i.e., the unconditional assertions of (the formulas) A and TA are deductively equivalent. In this sense Tarski's convention is satisfied. In view of the preceding paragraph we could hardly expect more.[21]

The distinctive feature of the truth operator, which it shares with the connectives F, $*$, $\rightarrow$, $+$, $\Rightarrow$ and $\cong$, is that its truth table assigns a truth value when every argument is undefined. On the Fregean principle that the reference of a complex symbol is a function of the references of the parts, this means that we cannot construe the reference of (3) in (4) as its truth value, for when e.g. 'Tom' fails to refer then (3) has no truth value, while (4) is false. Frege would explain this by noting that (3) occurs in (4) in an oblique context, namely in the clause

(7) that Tom is tall

and hence that on his principles its reference here is its ordinary sense, i.e. the proposition denoted by (7). The sentence (4) is thus meta-linguistic in the sense that it is not about Tom but rather the proposition (7). Another way of emphasizing this point is to note that one could regard (4) as splitting not into an operator

(8) It is true that...

and the sentence (3), but rather into a (meta-linguistic) predicate

(9) It is true...

and the clause (7), construed as a name of a proposition.

Finally, we have presented a theory of truth in which A and TA are of the same syntactic type, but which is clearly consistent. This is possible because we have in effect limited ourselves to only one way of referring to propositions, namely by prefixing 'that' to sentences expressing them. Just as one could not construct the liar paradox for sentences if quotation were the only way of referring to sentences, so here we cannot formulate the Liar for propositions. This limitation is not unimportant, for as Dummett has pointed out[22], the chief *use* of (9) and its synonyms is to endorse propositions referred to indirectly, as in

(10) Goldbach's conjecture is true.

Ultimately I think there can be no doubt that (9) rather than (8) is the more fundamental context for 'true', and that Tarski's work gives the most satisfying analysis of the concept of truth. Indeed, my remarks in the previous paragraph were predicated on this belief. Nevertheless, the present theory manages to capture a considerable part of the logic of truth in an elementary theory, and even gives rise to some interesting philosophical questions; this is surely sufficient justification for its study.[23]

One immediate application of the theory of truth is to the formalisation of the relation of presupposition. The latter has been defined by Strawson as follows[24]:

(if) S' is a necessary condition of the *truth or falsity* of S...(then) let us say...that S *presupposes* S'.

An examination of the tables of Section IV shows that

(11) $\models S \Rightarrow S'$

correctly renders this concept (the connective $\Rightarrow$ might be said to stand for 'material' presupposition on the analogy of material implication). $\Rightarrow$ is 'meta-linguistic' in the same sense as T, while the relation defined in (11) is explicitly meta-linguistic. Evidently a proposition will be truth-valueless iff it has some untrue presupposition.

The discussion of presupposition brings us back to the subject with which we began this paper, free logic. For Strawson's principle application of this notion is in connection with presuppositions of existence, of general terms in syllogistic and of singular terms in the predicate calculus.

In the final section of this essay I shall indicate one of several possible extensions of **U** to a full first-order logic (an extension which I believe to be the correct formalisation of Strawson's intuitions).

IX. A FREE LOGIC

The system to be defined will be called **UE**. The motivating thought in its construction will be that which has guided us throughout, i.e. the idea that truth-valuelessness arises from the presence of non-referring terms.

A morphology **M** for **UE** consists of the following disjoint well-ordered sets:

(i) A set $\mathbf{V_M}$ of *individual variables*,
(ii) a set $\mathbf{C_M}$ of *individual constants*,
(iii) for each $n < \omega$ a set $\mathbf{P}^n$ of n-ary *atomic predicates*,

together with the improper symbols

$$\supset, T, (,),$$

the primitive 0-ary atomic predicate

$$u$$

and the primitive 1-ary atomic predicate

$$E$$

(for existence). The elements of $\mathbf{V_M} \cup \mathbf{C_M}$ we call *individual symbols*. The set $At_{\mathbf{M}}$ of *atomic formulas* of M consists of all strings $Pt_1 \ldots t_n$ such that P is an n-ary atomic predicate, and for each i, t_i is an individual symbol. Any of the sets above may be empty, except that $At_{\mathbf{M}}$ will always contain at least u.

The set $\mathbf{W_M}$ of *formulas* of **M** is defined as in Section III, except that if A is a formula and $x \in \mathbf{V_M}$, then $(x)A$ is a formula. We adopt the definitions of Section III, as well as

D12. $(\exists x)\, A = \sim (x) \sim A$

A *domain* **D** is any non-empty set. An *assignment* α of values in **D** to the variables of **M** is any function with domain $\mathbf{V_M}$ and range **D**. We write $\alpha =_x \alpha'$ if α and α' differ at most at x.

An *interpretation* **I** of **M** in the domain **D** is a function which assigns to each n-ary atomic predicate an n-place function from **D** to $\{\mathbf{t}, \mathbf{f}\}$; in addition, to u the value **u** and to E the unary function whose value for every d in **D** is **t**; furthermore **I** assigns to every member of a subset $\mathbf{R_I}$ of $\mathbf{C_M}$ some element of **D**. The constants in $\mathbf{R_I}$ are called the *referring* constants of **M** on **I**.

The *truth-value function* determined by an interpretation **I** and an assignment α is a function $\mathbf{I}_\alpha$ defined on $\mathbf{W_M}$ and satisfying the following conditions:

(i) If P is an n-ary atomic predicate and $t_1, \ldots, t_n$ are in $\mathbf{V_M} \cup \mathbf{R_I}$, then $\mathbf{I}_\alpha(Pt_1 \ldots t_n) = \mathbf{I}(P)(d_1, \ldots, d_n)$ where if $t_i \in \mathbf{V_M}$ then $d_i = \alpha(t_i)$ and if $t_i \in R_I$ then $d_i = \mathbf{I}(t_i)$.

(ii) If $\mathbf{I}_\alpha(Et) \neq \mathbf{t}$, then $\mathbf{I}_\alpha(Et) = \mathbf{f}$.

(iii) $\mathbf{I}_\alpha(A \supset B) = \mathbf{t}$ iff $\mathbf{I}_\alpha(A) = \mathbf{f}$ or $\mathbf{I}_\alpha(B) = \mathbf{t}$;
$\mathbf{I}_\alpha(A \supset B) = f$ iff $\mathbf{I}_\alpha(A) = \mathbf{t}$ and $\mathbf{I}_\alpha(B) = \mathbf{f}$.

(iv) $\mathbf{I}_\alpha(TA) = \mathbf{t}$ iff $\mathbf{I}_\alpha(A) = \mathbf{t}$; otherwise, $\mathbf{I}_\alpha(TA) = \mathbf{f}$.

(v) $\mathbf{I}_\alpha((x)\, A) = \mathbf{t}$ iff for every $\alpha' =_x \alpha$, $\mathbf{I}_\alpha'(A) = \mathbf{t}$;
$\mathbf{I}_\alpha((x)\, A) = \mathbf{f}$ iff for some $\alpha' =_x \alpha$, $\mathbf{I}_\alpha'(A) = \mathbf{f}$.

(vi) $\mathbf{I}_\alpha(A) \in \{\mathbf{t}, \mathbf{u}, \mathbf{f}\}$.

An easy induction shows that if all the constants of A belong to $\mathbf{R_I}$, then for every α, $\mathbf{I}_\alpha(A) \in \{\mathbf{t}, \mathbf{f}\}$.[25] Thus we have followed our basic intuition to the extent of allowing truth-valuelessness to arise only from failure of reference. However, failure of reference need not always give rise to truth-value gaps. This is evident in the case of such formulas as Ea or TPa; in order to keep **UE** as general as possible, we have left cases of non-referring terms open except as required by (vi). Thus we might wish to have among our atomic predicates a predicate such as E, which would not be possible if we modified (i) to require that if any t_i is a non-referring constant then $\mathbf{I}_\alpha(Pt_1 \ldots t_n)=\mathbf{u}$. It has sometimes been suggested that some sentences about fictional characters might be true, despite the fact that these characters do not exist; this would also be ruled out by the suggested restriction. I recommend instead that special arrangements about existential presupposition should be made whenever a specific predicate or individual constant is brought into the theory, as is here the case with E.

The inference from a set Γ of assertions to an assertion (A) is *valid* iff for every domain, interpretation and assignment for which every member of Γ is correct, (A) is also correct.

The system **NUE** of natural deduction is similar to our earlier system **NU**. Indeed, the notion of proof is basically the same. The only difference consists in the addition of the following rules of direct consequence:

(x) **I**: $(x)\,A$ is a direct consequence of $(A_1), \ldots, (A_n)$ and a subproof whose only premises are $(A_1), \ldots, (A_n)$ and of which A is an element, provided that x does not occur free in any of $A_1, \ldots, A_n$.

(x) **E**: Let $A(t/x)$ be the result of substituting t for each free occurrence of x in A, unless t becomes bound thereby, in which case $A(t/x)=A$. Then $A(t/x)$ is a d.c. of $\underline{Et}$ and $(x)\,A$.

$\underline{(x)}$ **I**: $\underline{(x)}\ \underline{A}$ is a d.c. of $(A_1), \ldots, (A_n)$ and a subproof of which the latter are the only premises and of which $\underline{A}$ is an element, provided that x does not occur free in any of $A_1, \ldots, A_n$.

$\underline{(x)}$ **E**: $\underline{A(t/x)}$ is a d.c. of $\underline{Et}$ and $\underline{(x)}\ \underline{A}$.

E**I**: Ex is a d.c. of $\underline{A}$, for any variable x.

$\underline{E}$**E**: If $t_1, \ldots, t_n$ are all the terms which occur free in A, then A is a d.c. of $\underline{Et_1}, \ldots, \underline{Et_n}$ and $\underline{A}$.

NUE may be shown complete with respect to the semantics of this section by the usual extension of the methods of Section VII.[25]

In conclusion, I have tried to meet Scott's challenge by presenting a workable and philosophically interesting three-valued logic. The chief device which makes this possible is the distinction between two types of assertion, and the use of this distinction in proof theory and semantics. Much of course remains to be done. **UE** is, as mentioned, only one of several possible predicate calculi based on **U**. In addition, it is possible to generalize **U** in other ways, to a modal system and to an intuitionistic system (syntactically, the latter can be obtained by merely dropping the

Peirce rules from NU). But it should be clear that a three-valued logic can provide an interesting, feasible and fruitful approach to problems involving truth-value gaps. This is all I hoped to show.

University of California, Irvine

BIBLIOGRAPHY

[1] L. Åqvist, 'Reflections on the Logic of Nonsense', *Theoria* **28** (1962) 138–57.
[2] N. D. Belnap, Jr., 'Intensional Models for First-Degree Formulas', *Journal of Symbolic Logic* **32** (1967) 1–22.
[3] G. Birkhoff, *Lattice Theory*, 3rd ed., Providence, R.I., 1967.
[4] D. Bochvar 'Ob odnom trechznachnom ischislenii i evo primenenii k analyzu paradoksov klassicheskovo rashirennovo funktionalnovo ischislenii', *Matematicheskij Sbornik* **46** (n.s. 4) (1938) 287–308. See also review in *Journal of Symbolic Logic* **4** (1939) 98, and correction, *ibid.* **5** (1940) 119.
[5] A. Church, *Introduction to Mathematical Logic*, Vol. I, Princeton, N.J., 1956.
[6] H. B. Curry, *Foundations of Mathematical Logic*, New York 1963.
[7] M. E. Dummett, 'Truth', *Proceedings of the Aristotelian Society* **59** (1958–59) 141–62.
[8] F. B. Fitch, *Symbolic Logic*, New York 1952.
[9] G. Frege, 'Über Sinn und Bedeutung', *Zeitschrift für Philosophie und Philosophische Kritik* **100** (1892) 25–50.
[10] S. Hallden, *The Logic of Nonsense*, Uppsala 1949.
[11] L. Henkin, 'The Completeness of the First-Order Functional Calculus', *Journal of Symbolic Logic* **14** (1949) 159–66.
[12] D. Kaplan, 'The System R: Sentential Logic with Non-Denoting Sentences', unpublished manuscript, October 1967.
[13] S. C. Kleene, *Introduction to Metamathematics*, Princeton, N.J., 1952.
[14] S. Kripke, 'Semantical Considerations on Modal Logic', *Acta Philosophica Fennica* **16** (1963).
[15] J. Łukasiewicz, 'O Logice Trojwartosciowej', *Ruch Filozoficzny* **5** (1920) 169–71.
[16] G. C. Moisil, 'Les logiques non-chrysippiennes et leurs applications', *Acta Philosophica Fennica* **16** (1963) 137–52.
[17] R. Montague, 'Syntactical Treatments of Modality, with Corollaries on Reflexion Principles and Finite Axiomatizability', *Acta Philosophica Fennica* **16** (1963) 153–66.
[18] W. F. Sellars, *Science, Perception and Reality*, New York 1963.
[19] J. Słupecki, 'Der volle dreiwertige Aussagenkalkül', *Comptes rendus des séances de la Société des Sciences et des Lettres de Varsovie*, Cl. iii **29** (1936) 9–11.
[20] J. Słupecki, 'Pełny trojwartosciowej rachunek zda', *Annales Universitatis Mariae Curie-Sklodowska* (Lublin) **1** (1946) 193–209.
[21] P. F. Strawson, 'On Referring', *Mind* **59** (1950).
[22] P. F. Strawson, *Introduction to Logical Theory*, London 1952.
[23] A. Tarski, *Logic, Semantics, Metamathematics*, Oxford 1956.
[24] B. C. van Fraassen, 'Singular Terms, Truth-Value Gaps, and Free Logic', *Journal of Philosophy* **63** (1966) 481–95.

[25] B. C. van Fraassen, 'Presupposition, Implication and Self-Reference', *Journal of Philosophy* **65** (1968) 136–52.
[26] B. C. van Fraassen, 'Presuppositions, Supervaluations and Free Logic', in *The Logical Way of Doing Things* (ed. by K. Lambert), New Haven, Conn., 1969.

REFERENCES

* This article is based in part on material in my dissertation *Foundations of Three-Value Logic*, University of Pittsburgh, 1969. I should like to thank Mr. Michael Byrd for reading a preliminary draft and making a number of very helpful comments.
1 For example, see Scott's essay in this volume and Kripke [14]. All references are to the bibliography.
2 Frege [9], p. 41.
3 Strawson [21] and [22], Ch. 6.
4 Van Fraassen [25] and [26], among others. It was in response to Van Fraassen that the central themes of this essay were first developed.
5 Another response has been made by Kaplan in [12], in which he applies the methods of free quantificational logic to a propositional calculus with quantifiers.
6 The tables for conjunction, disjunction and negation are those of Łukasiewicz [15]. The implication operator is Kleene's [13], and the truth operator is found in Bochvar [4], Hallden [10] and Åqvist [1]. The present system **U** is perhaps closest to Åqvist's calculus **A**; the latter lacks only the constant *u* (see below). The interpretation of **U** is however different from that of any of the systems mentioned above.
7 Our *T* should not be confused with the connective *T* of Słupecki [19], which does for him what *u* does for us; i.e., *T*A is always undefined (see note 10).
8 See Bochvar [4] and Hallden [10].
9 Church [5], Ch. 1.
10 These tables are functionally complete. For we may define Łukasiewicz's *C* and *N* and Słupecki's *T* as follows:

$$CAB = (TA \supset B) \& (A \supset {*B})$$
$$NA = {\sim} A$$
$$TA = u \& (A \supset A).$$

By Słupecki [20] the tables for these connectives are functionally complete.
11 Frege [9], p. 27.
12 Strawson [21].
13 Cf. Belnap [2], § 3; also Birkhoff [3].
14 For a good survey, see Moisil [16].
15 It should be noted that if we adopt the 'meaninglessness' interpretation of **u** suggested in Section II, then the matter is rather different. For then we should want to regard a formula as expressing a proposition only when it has value; this in turn suggests that $[A]$ be defined as the *partial* function which is defined only on those **I** for which $\mathbf{I}(A) \neq \mathbf{u}$. If we then define meet and join as before, we obtain a non-trivial algebra, indeed a Boolean algebra. This algebra cannot, however, be conveniently extended to include an operation corresponding to *T*.
16 Fitch [8]. Fitch's presentation is slightly less rigorous than that adopted here.
17 The reason for calling **K** a rule of weakening has to do with a sequenzen-kalkül formulation of the system; the interested reader may consult Chapter II of my dissertation. A good discussion of Peirce's law is found in Curry [6], Ch. V. Cf. especially his Gentzen rule *Px*.

[18] The general technique is that of Henkin [11].
[19] Tarski [23], p. 187.
[20] E.g. Sellars in [18], Ch. 6.
[21] A good discussion of this problem is presented in Van Fraassen [25], p. 143.
[22] Dummett [7], p. 144.
[23] It is perhaps worth noting that in view of Montague's [17], the situation is exactly similar to that in modal logic.
[24] Strawson [22], p. 175.
[25] (added in proof) The remark on p. 138 is false, with the embarrassing result that the rule E*E*, wich reflects this remark, leads to inconsistency when added to our previous rules. For *u* has no free terms, hence by *u*I and *E*E it is a theorem. But then by *u*E every wff is a theorem.

The problem is that a constant like *u* has no place in a system with the 'Strawsonian' motivation of **UE**, and hence I was wrong to think of **UE** as, strictly speaking, an extension of **U**. A better course would be to give up functional completeness for the time being and take $\sim$ as primitive instead of *u*. Then when an appropriate description theory had been added, together with the requisite predicate constants, we could reproduce formally the informal definition of *u* given in Section I, or something like it. Kaplan suggests something like this in [12].

DANA SCOTT

ADVICE ON MODAL LOGIC

Everyone knows how much more pleasant it is to give advice than to take it. Everyone knows how little heed is taken of all the good advice he has to offer. Nevertheless, this knowledge seldom restrains anyone, least of all the present author. He has been noting the confusions, misdirections of emphasis, and duplications of effort current in studies of modal logic and is, by now, anxious to disseminate all kinds of valuable advice on the subject. Thus he is very happy that the Irving meeting has provided such a suitable and timely forum and hopes that all this advice can provoke some useful discussion – at least in self-defense. The time really seems to be ripe for a fruitful development of modal logic, if only we take care to purify and simplify the foundations. A quite flexible framework is indeed possible: the old puzzles can be brushed aside, and one can begin to provide meaningful applications.

Before embarking on details, here is one general piece of advice. One often hears that modal (or some other) logic is pointless because it can be translated into some simpler language in a first-order way. Take no notice of such arguments. There is no weight to the claim that the original system must therefore be replaced by the new one. What is essential is to single out important concepts and to investigate their properties. The fact that the real numbers can be defined in terms of sets is no argument for being interested in *arbitrary* sets. One must look among the sets for the significant ones and cannot be censured if one finds the intrinsic properties of the reals more interesting than any of their formulations in set theory. Of course if we can argue that set theory provides other significant concepts, then we may find some reason for going beyond the real numbers (and it is not hard to find the reasons!). But clearly this discussion cannot proceed on purely formal grounds alone.

This essay is divided into six sections. Section 1 discusses individuals: actual, possible, and virtual, Section 2 introduces possible worlds and their generalizations, Section 3 combines possible worlds and individuals to produce the fundamental notion of *individual concept*. Section 4 dis-

K.Lambert (ed.), Philosophical Problems in Logic.

cusses general intensional operators. Section 5 completes the discussion of the previous section by showing how to handle variable-binding operators. The final Section 6 brings out the distinction between incidence and equality needed for the problems of cross-world identifications. (The final discussion is not as satisfactory as the author hoped, and he looks forward to future developments.) The plan of writing was to set out the semantical framework for modal logic gradually – with (hopefully) adequate explanation – so, that all the good advice would not seem too authoritarian. In any case the various critical remarks were meant in the spirit of rational discussion. We want a synthesis of all good ideas and not just a triumph of one man's approach over another's.

I. INDIVIDUALS

What is an individual? A very good question. So good, in fact, that we should not even try to answer it. We could assume that being an individual is a primitive concept – that is harmless: any sufficiently clear concept can be made primitive. But maybe we do not want the individuals themselves but only some *constructs* or *tokens* representing the individuals. For the moment it does not matter: what is important is to agree that the individuals (or their legal representatives) can be collected together into one domain, a set that we may call D.

I feel it is important to be thinking of D as *fixed in advance*. This does not mean that one knows all the elements of D in any constructive sense, for one may only know some property specifying D. But much confusion results if one considers D vague. Any set can be enlarged by the introduction of new elements; but then a new set $D' \neq D$ obtains, and various results may undergo modification when interpreted relative to the new domain. Sometimes this change may take on the aspect of paradox if one forgets that $D' \neq D$. Maybe in the future we shall understand the logic of *potential totalities* (through intuitionism possibly?) but for the present our simple two-valued logic demands this idealization. Be not discouraged that from the first this idealism hangs in the air: ask yourself if you fully appreciate how powerful and flexible a tool two-valued logic really is. I feel that it is better to work out the idealized situation first – and then retrench later when one can value thoroughly what is gained and lost.

How big is D? Well, it should be rather large (at least *non-empty*) because we want D to be the domain of *possible individuals*. Here 'possible' means possible with respect to some a priori conception. The term 'conceivable' might be more to the point. In any case let me emphasize again that it is a relative notion. Of course we can conceive of individuals not in D, but that is neither here nor there. My only demand is that we conceive of at least *one* possible individual, because in general logic on the non-empty domain is simpler. Quantifiers over possibly empty domains will come in later in a more reasonable context.

It took me a very long time to concede the point that the notion of possible individual was reasonable. It was only after many discussions with the UCLA group (Montague, Kaplan, Cocchiarella and Kamp) that I finally saw the light. I was glad to note at the present meeting that others are coming to the same conclusions (van Fraassen and Lambert in particular). There are many examples to make the idea plausible: consider the following sentences. 'No two presidents of the United States ever looked alike.' 'All Nobel prize winners were equally deserving.' 'All readers of the novel will be as deeply moved as I.' We are playing here with the passage of time. Individuals (in this case persons) come into and go out of existence. Nevertheless it is meaningful to compare two of them existing at different times: not always two specific persons so that quantification over all the possible individuals is actually required. That is the difference between the first two of these sentences (in past tense) and the third (future). This is only one line of examples; once the problem is appreciated hundreds of examples come to mind.

We shall return to the distinction between *actual* and *possible* individuals below in Section 5. In this section we wish to emphasize another distinction: *possible* vs. *virtual*. It has been Quine who has recently popularized virtual entities. Forgive the word 'entity', since Quine would seem to be happier to treat them merely as *façon de parler* with all references thereto avoidable by contextual definition. That seems to me to be a mistake of emphases or maybe an error of shortsightedness. The possibility of introducing virtual entities is unlimited and for the most part relatively unexplored. They are not to be regarded as ghosts but rather as *ideal objects* introduced to enhance the regularity of our language. By using the names of these entities we often find a simple formulation that avoids a confusing proliferation of cases. In the ordinary theory of real numbers $\pm\infty$ are excellent examples of useful ideal points; in projective geometry, the points at infinity; in set theory, the virtual classes. Of course each of the above mentioned notions can be eliminated (at the cost of much longer statements) by contextual definitions. We must now examine my reasons for advising not making contextual elimination the central feature of these concepts.

My most outstanding reservation centers on the feeling that I do not know what the general theory of contextual definitions is. I even have some doubt that there is such a theory. Maybe I am just being stubborn as I have often been in the past, but I do not know of any really serious study of the problem. This is not to say that Quine has not given us some important examples of the use of contextual definitions. Rather I would propose a somewhat more neutral course that will allow us to think about the question in a clear way before deciding on the final answer. The point is that the case by case presentation of the contextual eliminations (the cases being governed by the possible contexts) always makes me worry that some type of discontinuity may creep in, that is to say, in one context the virtual object may behave as one kind of thing whereas in another place it may be quite different. Well, that is not unreasonable: no object stands in all the same relationships to all other objects. What disturbs me rather is that the contextual method makes it too easy to allow the entities to be fickle.

What is to be done? Simply this: let us think of the expressions for virtual objects as actually denoting (abstract) entities. Instead of *definitions* we take *axioms* (maybe just by using '$\leftrightarrow$' in place of 'for' – working in the object language of course!). It is a heavier commitment, no doubt about it. Thus if something goes wrong, we have to face the fact that our axioms are inconsistent – we cannot so easily confuse the issue by changing some clause of a 'definition' and calling it harmless. That is a negative advantage. A positive advantage may also be possible: in the case of virtual classes I have shown in my paper on descriptions that the axioms can be made simpler and more elegant than the definition. I feel that this makes virtual classes easier to understand. Of course an elimination metatheorem can be justified on the basis of the axioms; this may often be the case. Thus my advice is to leave the elimination problems to the *development* of the theory rather than having them complicate the *formalization.*

The next question is: should we quantify over virtual objects? I think the answer should be a firm no. Quantification (or the ranges of the bound variables) should only be over the possible individuals. If we have come to value the virtual entities so highly that we want to quantify over them, then we have passed to a *new* theory with a *new* ontology (and with new virtuals also!) The role of the virtual entities is to make clear the structure of the basic domain D, not to introduce a whole new collection of problems. That is why we are happier when references to the virtuals can be eliminated. But maybe virtuals can also be used to simplify the introduction of the *primitive* structure into D, so elimination may not always be possible. Still they must take second place to the individuals in D.

The kind of quantification just rejected was quantification over *all* the virtuals. It may very well be that quantification over *part* of them is useful. Let us take the theory of actual and virtual classes as an example. Every actual class has its *cardinal number*. If a, b are actual classes (sets), let us write $a \approx b$ to mean that a one-one correspondence exists (as an actual relation). Then the cardinal number of a set a can be defined by the equation

$$|a| = \{x : x \approx a\}.$$

In the usual theories of classes $|a|$ is generally virtual but *not* actual.

Among the virtual classes we can define what it means to be a cardinal in the obvious way:

$$\text{Card}\,[\tau] \leftrightarrow \exists x\,[\tau = |x|],$$

where τ is a term and x is not free in τ.

Would it not be rather pleasant to be able to have *variables* ranging over cardinals, say German letters $\mathfrak{m}$, $\mathfrak{n}$..., so that various existence theorems could be stated in the usual way? The answer is simple: yes, you may do so and even not compromise your views on virtual objects. Obviously we simply let

$$\forall \mathfrak{m}\, \Phi(\mathfrak{m}) \leftrightarrow \forall x\, \Phi(|x|),$$

and

$$\exists \mathfrak{m}\, \Phi(\mathfrak{m}) \leftrightarrow \exists x\, \Phi(|x|).$$

The meaning is clearly what was intended, and we see that the quantification is no worse than the usual quantification over sets. The same approach can clearly be applied to quantification over any portion of the virtuals that can be *enumerated* or *indexed* by the sets with the aid of some definable operation like $|a|$. By this method one never quantifies over all the virtuals, however, for no matter what operation $\varphi(a)$ one takes the virtual class $\tau = \{x : x \notin \varphi(x)\}$ is such that $\neg \exists y [\tau = \varphi(y)]$. Still the method seems useful and natural.

In summary then we are distinguishing between *virtual*, *possible*, and *actual*. Let us use V for the domain of virtual objects, D for possible, A for actual, where we assume for simplicity that

$$A \subseteq D \subseteq V.$$

The distinction between A and D does not arise in the usual systems but becomes very critical in modal logic. (In fact, A will have to be replaced by a whole family of domains $A_i \subseteq D$ for $i \in I$). However, even in non-modal logic it can be useful to make the separation (cf. the work of Cocchiarella and of Lambert).

Note that we have already been using the relation of *equality* (=) between individuals – even on V. This is just and proper. Equality *is* a logical notion. Just because people have been in the past confused about the properties of equality does not mean that the notion is basically unclear. We shall be discussing it fully in connection with the modal notions.

II. POSSIBLE WORLDS

This is not the place to discuss where the idea of possible worlds came from, it is sufficient to remark that the recent works of Kanger, Montague, Hintikka, and Kripke have clearly established the usefulness of the notion. Indeed the idea seems so useful that I wish to advocate keeping in mind an extension of the concept, that makes the method much more flexible, or so it seems to me.

My advice is to use the principle of *indexical expressions* of Carnap-Bar-Hillel. The possible worlds thought of as particular collections of individuals with or without additional structure give only one aspect of the idea. Any system of structures can be indexed by the elements of some suitable set, usually in many different ways. Thus we are going to take a fixed set I of these indices and in the first instance index the system of actual individuals by having possibly distinct $A_i \subseteq D$ for each $i \in I$. It is important not to assume a one-one correspondence between the A_i and the i, for the elements of the set I may possess significant structure not at all reflected in the change from one A_i to another. This is why I reject taking either the models of Montague-Kripke (earlier writings) or the model sets of Hintikka as fundamental. This point has to be argued a little more closely. It is not sufficient to point out that with the models or model sets we can assume enough distinctions to gain the *effect* of any index set (by using several distinct copies of a set or by introducing special predicates into the language) for that is only to admit that the method of indices is in fact more fundamental.

Let us see how the indices work. The point is that in the expressions of our language we make some indefinite reference to the indices – hence the terminology. Already we can give one example, though better examples come soon. This example has to do with quantification. We have the one quantifier $\forall x$ which is interpreted as ranging over D. We now introduce the 'actual' quantifier $\forall .x$, where the dot is meant to suggest an indefinite index. Thus even if we know the meaning of the predicate P we cannot say whether

$$\forall .x\, P(x)$$

is true or false. However, if we specify an $i \in I$, then *relative* to this index the sentence assumes a truth value: namely it is *true* if $P(a)$ is true for all $a \in A_i$. Until we specify the $i \in I$, the range of the quantified variable is not known.

The above example supplies us with a statement whose truth-value is not constant but varies as a function of $i \in I$. This situation is easily appreciated in the context of time-dependent statements; that is, in the case where I represents the instants of time. Obviously the same statement can be true at one moment and false at another. For more general situations one must not think of the $i \in I$ as anything as simple as instants of time or even possible worlds. In general we will have

$$i = (w, t, p, a, \ldots)$$

where the index i has many *coordinates*: for example, w is a *world*, t is a *time*, $p = (x, y, z)$ is a (3-dimensional) *position* in the world, a is an *agent*, etc. All these coordinates can be varied, possibly independently, and thus affect the truth values of statements which have indirect references to these coordinates.

The question arises as to why we cannot simply make the references direct and reduce the logic of indexical expressions to ordinary logic. Well, the answer is that we just do not speak that way. All kinds of statements have indirect references to the here, the now, the I (first person). And these statements have a logic; it is possible to say that some of them are true by virtue of their syntactical form. Thus in view of the commonness and simplicity of these statements, we are certainly obliged to investigate their intrinsic logic. Of course a translation into a more elementary language may help for certain results, but that does not mean that the more involved language has been eliminated or made uninteresting. It is somewhat like the idea of *typical ambiguity*: we need not specify the exact type of variables – only the relative distances between levels. Many statements are true at all levels, and it is only painful to force oneself to carry along the exact levels in the notation.

One could call the *$i \in I$ points of reference* because to determine the truth of an expression the point of reference must be established. Previously I had suggested that terminology as more neutral and more suggestive of the proper generality than *possible worlds*. Maybe *index* is just as good a term, though it seems to me to make them sound rather insignificant. In any case in making up interpretations of the language the set I, along with $A_i \subseteq D \subseteq V$, is to be fixed in advance. Remember it is not fair to shift the size of I in the middle of a discussion (or to invoke unsuspected coordinates) and then deride the logic as inconsistent or counter-intuitive. Such arguments may, if they have any serious content, show an interpretation to be inadequate for representing a complicated situation. That is to say a *particular* interpretation may be discredited, but that does not discredit the *method* of constructing interpretations.

In summary then we conclude that the truth values of statements vary with the $i \in I$. In order to state in a convenient way the connections between statements and their parts some notation is in order. Let us first make the truth-values visible: we write 1 for *true* and 0 for *false*. The reason for this choice of notation is that $2 = \{0, 1\}$ is a simple and readily available symbol for the set of the two truth values. Next associated with a statement Φ will be a *function*, call it $\|\Phi\|$, the *value* of Φ in the interpretation, defined on I with values in 2. In other words we shall write the equation

$$\|\Phi\|_i = 1$$

to mean that Φ *is true at i*. Other notations are possible, and some variants are discussed later. Note that we use the subscript notation f_i interchangeably with the function-value notation $f(i)$. Sometimes we may wish to refer to the set of all functions from I into 2; it is denoted by 2^I, and we may write

$$\|\Phi\| \in 2^I$$

whereas

$$\|\Phi\|_i \in 2$$

for $i \in I$.

We have already in effect agreed that our language will contain the usual propositional connectives $\neg$, $\vee$, $\wedge$, $\rightarrow$, $\leftrightarrow$ and the quantifiers $\forall$, $\forall.$, $\exists$, and $\exists.$ with other operators to be discussed later. In explaining the meaning of these symbols we give the usual kinds of semantical definitions as follows:

$$(\neg) \qquad \|\neg \Phi\|_i = 1 \quad \text{iff} \quad \|\Phi\|_i = 0,$$

$$(\vee) \qquad \|[\Phi \vee \Psi]\|_i = 1 \quad \text{iff} \quad \|\Phi\|_i = 1 \quad \text{or} \quad \|\Psi\|_i = 1,$$

$$(\wedge) \qquad \|[\Phi \wedge \Psi]\|_i = 1 \quad \text{iff} \quad \|\Phi\|_i = 1 \quad \text{and} \quad \|\Psi\|_i = 1,$$

and similarly for the clauses of the truth definition ($\rightarrow$) and ($\leftrightarrow$). Note that we do not have to say $\|\neg\Phi\|_i = 0$ otherwise in ($\neg$) because we have already agreed to the two-valued character of the logic.

To be able to interpret the quantifiers I would advise introducing *constants* $\bar{a}$ into the language corresponding to *all* the $a \in V$. Of course the correspondence between a and $\bar{a}$ must be one-one. We can then write:

$$(\forall) \qquad \|\forall x\, \Phi(x)\|_i = 1 \quad \text{iff} \quad \|\Phi(\bar{a})\|_i = 1 \quad \text{for all} \quad a \in D$$

$$(\forall.) \qquad \|\forall . x\, \Phi(x)\|_i = 1 \quad \text{iff} \quad \|\Phi(\bar{a})\|_i = 1 \quad \text{for all} \quad a \in A_i .$$

Similarly for ($\exists$) and ($\exists.$). Now I know that some people do not like to have their languages made uncountable with too heavy a 'telephone book' of individual names. That was one of the reasons Tarski introduced his version of the definition of satisfaction. I have worked with both kinds of definitions and have found the style with individual constants *much easier* to *communicate* to those unpracticed in set theory. For one thing the clause of the truth definition is shorter.

So far we have only discussed the connections between and quantification of propositions. The nature of the interpretation of atomic formulas and terms (like descriptions) deserves a section of its own.

III. INDIVIDUAL CONCEPTS

Why should we not throw ourselves into the midst of the battle at once by discussing *definite descriptions.* They illustrate all the problems and lead directly to the general operators. So first of all what is the notation? We have had ℩, *T*, *U* to suggest *the* and *unique*, but I do not care for any of these. It is a matter of taste, but since I am using inverted sans-serif ∀ and ∃ for the quantifiers, I have finally decided to use an (inverted?) sans-serif capital I to suggest the word *individual.* (Actually *T* is not bad, but then what about *T* and *F*, or ⊤ and ⊥, for the truth values?) The semantics is rather obvious no matter what the notation, for we have:

$$(\mathsf{I}) \qquad \|\mathsf{I}x\, \Phi(x)\|_i = a \quad \text{iff} \quad \{a\} = \{b \in D : \|\Phi(\bar{b})\|_i = 1\}.$$

That is to say, given $i \in I$ so that we know how to evaluate $\|\Phi(\bar{b})\|_i$ for each $b \in D$ we can ask whether there is a *unique* b making the formula true. If so, call it the individual a and that will be the *value* of the descriptive phase *relative to i.* Hence, $\|\mathsf{I}x\Phi(x)\|$ is being defined as a *function* from I into D. But what kind of a function? What of the *improper* descriptive phrases? Answer: the function is most naturally taken as a PARTIAL FUNCTION; improper descriptions have 'undefined' values.

The opinion just presented is a change of mind over what I have been advocating previously (even in my original Irvine lecture!). It was only when I started to set down in an informal, conversational way my accumulated suggestions that I saw how to take full advantage of the idea (yet to be explained here in detail) of *individual concepts.* The scheme will become clearer as we go along.

Note that along with I we also have the operator I. which picks out actual individuals and is defined in the obvious way by:

$$(\mathsf{I}.) \qquad \|\mathsf{I}.x\, \Phi(x)\|_i = a \quad \text{iff} \quad \{a\} = \{b \in A_i : \|\Phi(\bar{b})\|_i = 1\},$$

where we take the value to be *undefined* in case there is no a satisfying the condition on the right. Of course this operator is not really fundamental because it is so easily defined in terms of the other notions:

$$\text{I}.x\, \Phi(x) = \text{I}x\exists.y\, [y = x \wedge \Phi(y)].$$

This last remark reminds us that we have not discussed equality. As usual our language has *terms* and *formulas* combined by the usual particles as well as by some unusual ones yet to be introduced. In particular two terms τ and σ can be combined into an equation $\tau = \sigma$ which is a formula. We are going to be able to evaluate every well-formed expression without free variables, so we may assume that we know what $\|\tau\|$ and $\|\sigma\|$ are: namely partial functions from I into —— into what? So far for descriptions the values have only been in D but in general the values should clearly lie in V. Let us write $V^{(I)}$ for the set of *partial* functions whereas V^I would denote the set of *total* functions, so that

$$\|\tau\|, \|\sigma\| \in V^{(I)}.$$

Now for equality:

(=) $\|\tau = \sigma\|_i = 1$ iff either $\|\tau\|_i$ and $\|\sigma\|_i$ are both defined and equal or neither are defined.

Yes, yes, I can hear the objections being shouted from all corners. If one is going to use undefined terms why not undefined truth values? Is not that more natural? Maybe so, but I have yet to see a really workable three-valued logic. I know it can be defined, and at least four times a year someone comes up with the idea anew, but it has *not* really been developed to the point where one could say it is pleasant to work with. Maybe the day will come, but I have yet to be convinced. So my advice is to continue with the two-valued logic because it is easy to understand and easy to use in applications; then when someone has made the other logic workable a switch should be reasonably painless.

On the basis of (=) it is obvious that the following two formulas are always true for all $i \in I$:

$$\tau = \tau, \quad \text{and} \quad [\tau = \sigma \wedge \tau = \theta \rightarrow \sigma = \theta],$$

which was the reason for the choice of the definition. As will become apparent as we go along the following generally *fails*:

$$\tau = \sigma \wedge \Phi(\tau) \rightarrow \Phi(\sigma),$$

which seems disturbing. However, an important special case does hold. First we must say what to do with (virtual) individual constants:

$$\|\bar{a}\|_i = a$$

for all $a \in V$. That is surely the intended meaning of $\bar{a}$. Now it is easy to check that

$$\bar{a} = \bar{b} \wedge \Phi(\bar{a}) \rightarrow \Phi(\bar{b})$$

is always true. In particular this slightly weaker statement also holds:

$$\forall x \, \forall y \, [x = y \wedge \Phi(x) \rightarrow \Phi(y)].$$

To understand better how the semantics goes let us take over (more or less) the following terminology from Carnap: we call the elements of 2^I *propositional concepts* and those of $V^{(I)}$ *individual concepts*. Note that

$$A_i^{(I)} \subseteq D^{(I)} \subseteq V^{(I)}$$

so that we have a classification of our individual concepts parallel to that for individuals. We call these things *concepts* because they have values depending on the index or point of reference in I and together form a coherent range of values, that is to say a *function*. Such a stringing together of individuals (or truth values) gives us, not a single individual, but a concept of an individual relative to the point of reference. Everyone is familiar with this from such old descriptive phrases as 'the present king of France'. Note that V is constructed *first* and $V^{(I)}$ constructed *second* to be able to evaluate terms. That is to say the individual concept is a semantical construct rather than a primitive ontological notion.

To repeat: for terms τ and formulas Φ:

$$\|\tau\| \in V^{(I)} \quad \text{and} \quad \|\Phi\| \in 2^I .$$

Thus $\|\tau\|$ is somewhat like Frege's *sense* while $\|\tau\|_i$ is like *denotation.* But not exactly. Let us not get into that discussion here. Maybe it would be better to be a little more like Carnap and call $\|\tau\|$ the *intension* of τ and $\|\tau\|_i$ the *extension* of τ at $i \in I$. The basic principle of our semantics is:

> *The intension of a whole expression is determined by the intensions of its parts.*

The same may very well *not* be true of the extension. This is how we explain the 'paradox' of equality: the natural reading of $\tau = \sigma$ is only that

τ and σ have the same extension (if any) relative to the current point of reference. This does *not* in general imply equality of intensions. Hence we cannot have a general substitutivity of equals – unless like true individual constants the intension is indeed a *constant* function.

Returning now for a moment to descriptions we note the validity of:

$$\forall y\, [y = \text{I}x\, \Phi(x) \leftrightarrow \forall x\, [x = y \leftrightarrow \Phi(x)]].$$

This is the basic property of descriptions that has been advocated by many of us (Hintikka, Van Fraassen, Lambert, the present author, to name only a few), and by now it seems natural. According to the way I have treated individual concepts we also have a definite result for the improper descriptions. We see that $\|\text{I}x[x \neq x]\|$ is the *totally undefined* function in $V^{(I)}$; let us call it $*$. This concept $* \in V^{(I)}$ works very much like Frege's null-entity and it now seems to me to be *more natural* than an *arbitrary* choice of a null element in $V \sim D$. For one thing it is uniquely determined: it can be called a semantical construct, which seems to put it in its proper place. We find, however, the same valid sentence we had before when $* \in V \sim D$:

$$\neg\, \exists y\, [y = \text{I}x\, \Phi(x)] \rightarrow \text{I}x\, \Phi(x) = \text{I}x\, [x \neq x].$$

IV. INTENSIONAL OPERATORS

So far we have been moving along on a very pure logical level: all the notions (except for individual constants) have been logical notions. It is now time to discuss the *non-logical* notions and to be led by this discussion even to further logical notions.

What about (atomic) predicates? Let us discuss binary relations as a prime example. Our only example so far has been equality and it is somewhat special. Note first, however, that just as with equality we should allow for expressions

$$\tau\, \mathbf{R}\, \sigma$$

where τ and σ may be arbitrary terms. (We certainly want to be able to say such things as 'Yvonne is the wife of the present king of France'.) Now this brings up the question as how we are to interpret $\mathbf{R}$; call the interpretation $\|\mathbf{R}\|$. Is it to be a relation between individuals *or* individual concepts? Answer: the latter. Why? Because even if we only start with individual relations, we will be able to define an intensional relation that depends on the whole intension of each of the arguments. (This will be obvious as soon as we have the modal operators.) Therefore, in general we should take

$$\|\mathbf{R}\| \in (2^I)^{V(I) \times V(I)}$$

so that in the corresponding clause in the truth definition we have

$$(\mathbf{R}) \qquad \|\tau\, \mathbf{R}\, \sigma\| = \|\mathbf{R}\| \, (\|\tau\|, \|\sigma\|).$$

Similarly for predicates with more places. Note that the subscript i is unnecessary here because we took the values of $\|\mathbf{R}\|$ to belong to 2^I.

The main reason for making general predicates so complicated was not simply to torture the reader but to make our logic *general*. When we know that a formula is *logically valid* (that is, true in all interpretations relative to all points of reference of the interpretation), then it should remain valid when *formulas* are substituted for *predicate letters*. There is no other convention that is reasonable. But that does not keep us from discussing special kinds of predicates, as is clear.

One special kind of predicate is *extensional*. The best examples come from ordinary relations $R \subseteq V \times V$. (Remember: $2 < +\infty$, so that our relations must be defined over all of V.) Let us write $\bar{R}$ for the constant in the language that corresponds to R in analogy with individuals. Then

$$(\bar{R}) \qquad \|\tau\, \bar{R}\, \sigma\|_i = 1 \quad \text{iff} \quad (\|\tau\|_i, \|\sigma\|_i) \in R.$$

Note for this atomic formula to be true, both $\|\tau\|_i$ and $\|\sigma\|_i$ must be defined. This convention was not what we chose to do for equality – because the special role of equality favors a different convention making for more regularity among the valid formulas. (An interesting sidelight: if all our atomic formulas were either made with $=$ or various $\bar{R}$'s and if our only terms were either variables or descriptions, then descriptions could be entirely eliminated. In general this is not so.) For example the *extensionality principle* (for $\bar{R}$) reads

$$\tau = \tau' \wedge \sigma = \sigma' \wedge \tau\, \bar{R}\, \sigma \rightarrow \tau'\, \bar{R}\, \sigma'.$$

Not every extensional predicate in this sense comes from an ordinary R. The reader can easily work out for himself other examples, and we shall return to this question below.

Intensional relations do not spring to mind as easily as do intensional propositional operators. The simplest example is $\Box$, *necessity*, defined by

$$(\Box) \qquad \|\Box\Phi\|_i = 1 \quad \text{iff} \quad \|\Phi\|_j = 1 \quad \text{for all} \quad j \in I$$

This means nothing more or less than true in all possible worlds. What should we call it? *Logical necessity* does not seem correct since it depends on I (as do the values $\|\mathbf{R}\|$). How about *universal necessity*? Because we are in effect quantifying over our universe I. Whatever we call it we find that it is an S5 modal operator, and a very useful one. Of course possibility is defined in the dual way and we do not need to write down here the clause $(\Diamond)$ of the truth definition.

If we want we can say that $\Box$ has a value $\|\Box\|$ just as we did for $\|R\|$. Indeed $\|\Box\|$ is of the same logical type as $\|\neg\|$:

$$\|\Box\|, \|\neg\| \in (2^I)^{2^I}$$

They are mappings from propositional concepts to propositional concepts. The difference is that one is extensional and the other is not. Note that we can write

$$\|\Box\Phi\| = \|\Box\| (\|\Phi\|)$$

(without subscripts!) making our dogma about intensions quite evident.

Now that our logical notation is becoming more interesting it is useful to examine certain compound phases: for example $\Box\tau = \sigma$. By definition we have:

$$\|\Box\tau = \sigma\|_i = 1 \quad \text{iff} \quad \|\tau\|_j = \|\sigma\|_j \quad \text{for all} \quad j \in I,$$

where we agree that the equation on the right holds in case *both* sides are undefined. That is to say $\|\Box\tau = \sigma\|$ is the concept of the true proposition iff $\|\tau\| = \|\sigma\|$ which means $\|\tau\|$ and $\|\sigma\|$ are the *same* individual concept. Let us introduce a symbol for this notion:

$$\tau \equiv \sigma \leftrightarrow \Box\tau = \sigma .$$

Thus we are distinguishing between extensional equality $(\tau = \sigma)$ and intensional equality $(\tau \equiv \sigma)$. Let us call the stronger notion *identity* for short.

In view of our dogma of intensions (which can be formally justified from the semantics) we find that if τ and σ have no free variables, then:

$$\tau \equiv \sigma \wedge \Phi(\tau) \rightarrow \Phi(\sigma)$$

is valid for identity; while the corresponding principle for equality fails. Similarly if Φ and Ψ are without free variables and Θ' results from Θ by replacing occurrences of Φ by Ψ, then

$$\Box[\Phi \leftrightarrow \Psi] \wedge \Theta \rightarrow \Theta'$$

also holds. Thus our logic has a certain degree of extensionality: *logically equivalent* formulas are substitutible. Some people feel that a truly intensional logic should reject even this principle. I have not seen a clear semantical discussion of such a logic. Usually there is a confusion between propositional operators and predicates of sentences; that is, the object language must formalize a part of syntax. Even then I have not seen any reasonable general system. My advice is to work for a while on this intermediate intensional level, because I shall try to argue in the final section that there is much to do involving notions of interest.

The next most interesting combination involves $\Box$ and $\forall$. This is valid:

$$\Box \forall x\, \Phi(x) \leftrightarrow \forall x\, \Box \Phi(x),$$

This is *not*:

$$\Box \forall. x\, \Phi(x) \leftrightarrow \forall. x\, \Box \Phi(x),$$

indeed, *neither direction* is valid for $\forall.$. The counterexamples are easy to come by. There has been so much fuss over these principles in the last few years, and it was all unnecessary: there *are* two kinds of quantifiers with *different* properties. All we needed to do was to make the semantics clear. (This point has been made by Kripke and others – but it does not hurt to make it again.)

To make the counterexample more obvious for the quantifier problem just mentioned it is useful to discuss extensional predicates again. Suppose that to each $i \in I$ we attach a relation $R_i \subseteq V \times V$ with possibly different R_i's for different i's. (We can treat R as a relation-valued function). Then we can introduce into our language a constant $\tilde{\bar{R}}$ (the bar $\bar{}$ suggests a *constant* relation, the tilde $\tilde{}$ a *variable* relation) where the meaning is given by

$$(\tilde{\bar{R}}) \qquad \|\tau\, \tilde{\bar{R}}\, \sigma\|_i = 1 \quad \text{iff} \quad (\|\tau\|_i, \|\sigma\|_i) \in R_i$$

Indeed $A_i \subseteq D$ is just such a variable one-place predicate so we can write

$$(\tilde{\bar{A}}) \qquad \|\tilde{\bar{A}}\tau\|_i = 1 \quad \text{iff} \quad \|\tau\|_i \in A_i .$$

We then find the following valid:

$$\forall.x\, \Phi(x) \leftrightarrow \forall x\, [\tilde{A}x \rightarrow \Phi(x)],$$

that is to say $\forall.$ is a *restricted quantifier*. Now it is easy to see why

$$[\tilde{A}x \rightarrow \Box \Phi(x)]$$

and

$$\Box [\tilde{A}x \rightarrow \Phi(x)]$$

are independent, which accounts for the phenomenon we noted.

The use of variable predicates in the way just indicated seems to me to be preferable to the manner in which Van Fraassen suggested using what he calls *logical space*. If I understand his method, he treats D (which may as well be equal to V for the moment) as a set of abstract place-holders for individuals. I imagine something like a giant egg crate. Defined on this space are certain *fixed* predicates. The actual individuals are thought of as being mapped (or stored) into the set D. Next a family of transformation $T = \{t_i : i \in I\}$ is given, and we can follow an individual around D by seeing how $a \in D$ is transformed into $t_i(a)$. Of course, a and $t_i(a)$ have different properties with respect to the fixed predicates. There is just something about this idea that strikes me as being inconvenient – or at least not general enough. I would imagine we can obtain the same effect by replacing the fixed relation R by the family R_i of relations defined by

$$a\, R_i\, b \leftrightarrow t_i(a)\, R\, t_i(b)$$

and by keeping the individuals fixed in place. The point is that I feel that Van Fraassen is mixing the variability of the predicates together with the interpretation of his modal operator. These are things that I feel should be kept separate, and so my advice is to adopt the kind of model structure presented here where the modal operators can be treated in isolation.

For example we may assume that I is a system with a binary mode of composition $\circ$, where, if we like the transformational approach, we may assume

$$t_j(t_i(a)) = t_{i \circ j}(a).$$

We can then define a propositional operator $\boxed{\rightarrow}$ by:

$$(\boxed{\rightarrow}) \qquad \|\boxed{\rightarrow}\, \Phi\|_i = 1 \quad \text{iff} \quad \|\Phi\|_{i \circ j} = 1 \quad \text{for all } j \in I.$$

That will give a fairly interesting operator, but of course it is one of a rather special kind – it would come up in tense logic for example. It is only one of many different types, however.

More generally let $\rho \subseteq I \times I$ be a binary relation on I, corresponding to ρ is the operator $\boxed{\varrho}$ defined by

$$(\boxed{\rho}) \qquad \|\boxed{\rho}\Phi\|_i = 1 \quad \text{iff} \quad \|\Phi\|_j = 1 \quad \text{for all} \quad j \in I \quad \text{where } i\,\rho\,j.$$

In other words, ϱ is simply an *alternative relation* on possible worlds. We are by now very familiar with all the work done on this type of operator. It must be stressed, however, that this is not the only way to obtain interesting operators; though it does include the previous example.

The simplest example of an operator which is not naturally specified by an alternative relation occurs in tense logic. Suppose I is taken as time (i.e. the set of real numbers). We define the *progressive tense operator* $\boxed{\leftrightarrow}$ by:

$$(\boxed{\leftrightarrow}) \qquad \|\boxed{\leftrightarrow}\,\Phi\|_i = 1 \text{ iff there is an open interval } J \subseteq I \text{ with } i \in J \text{ such that } \|\Phi\|_j = 1 \quad \text{for all} \quad j \in J\,.$$

Long ago McKinsey and Tarski showed that the logic of $\boxed{\leftrightarrow}$ is exactly S4. Now on some other index set I we can capture S4 with the help of an alternative relation – but on the ordinary reals there is no way of obtaining the same $\boxed{\leftrightarrow}$.

It is by now only a small step to the most general monadic propositional operator. Associate with each $i \in I$ a family $\mathscr{I}_i$ of *subsets* of I. We then can define the corresponding operator:

$$(\boxed{\mathscr{I}}) \qquad \|\boxed{\mathscr{I}}\Phi\|_i = 1 \quad \text{iff} \quad \{j \in I : \|\Phi\|_j = 1\} \in \mathscr{I}_i,$$

which we see is only a trivial reformulation of the statement that

$$\|\boxed{\mathscr{I}}\| \in (2^I)^{2I}.$$

But somehow it reads differently in terms of sets. We note that in the example of $\boxed{\leftrightarrow}$, the family $\mathscr{I}_i$ should be taken as the collection of all subsets of I containing the point $\mathscr{I}_i$ in their interiors; the neighborhoods of i in other terminology.

Among all the various operators $\boxed{\mathscr{I}}$ it is clear that only very few should be called *logical operators* – that is those that do not depend on the structure of I. With a proper definition (invariance under permutation of I, for example) we can no doubt show that the only logical operators are $\neg$, $\neg\neg$, $\Box$, and $\Diamond$. This of course does not mean that the others are uninteresting – far from it. Here is what I consider one of the biggest mistakes of all in modal logic: concentration on a system with just *one* modal operator. The only way to have any philosophically significant results in deontic logic or epistemic logic is to combine those operators with: tense operators (otherwise how can you formulate principles of change?); the logical operators (otherwise how can you compare the relative with the absolute?); the operators like *historical* or *physical* necessity (otherwise how can you relate the agent to his environment?); and so on and so on. But where to stop? This list can be extended further and further. One must stop somewhere, but to stop the list at *one* is obviously missing out on something important. The point I am trying to make is that the semantics being explained here allows for several operators side by side in a simple convenient, and natural way: one has only to think what coordinates $i=(w, t, p, a, \ldots)$ one wants. Furthermore one should not forget the logical operators.

This last point is one on which I am somewhat critical of Hintikka. He uses only one operator (which I would write here as $\boxed{\rho}$) and tries to express the various conditions for substitutivity and existence in terms of equations $\boxed{\varrho}^n\tau=\sigma$ with iterated modalities. I feel that this is making the alternative relation do too much work: the fundamental condition for substitutivity is $\Box\tau=\sigma$. The conditions involving the weaker relation should be presented as *metatheorems* concerning *special* contexts (special formulas $\Phi(\tau)$) rather than being emphasized as part of the basic semantics. It seems to me that the present approach provides quite a suitable place for Hintikka's useful and important insights.

V. VARIABLE BINDING OPERATORS

Up to this point we have been discussing at most intensional relations or intensional operators on propositions. Though it is painful, a certain greater degree of generality is called for. In particular the extensional operators like the quantifiers and the discriptive operators have intensional counterparts. Let us consider first an operator $ which binds one variable and operates on one term and one formula: we can employ it in the language with the following format:

$$\$x\,[\tau(x), \Phi(x)].$$

Now we have our choice: the result is either a *term* or a *formula.*

Let us take the first case where \$ makes terms. Now the values of this compound term must be allowed to be virtual (cf. the expression

$$\bigcup_{x \in A} \tau(x)$$

in class theory: its being a set depends on A and $\tau(x)$ in an essential way). But we have an intensional logic so (virtual) individual concepts are called for as values. Thus

$$\|\$x\,[\tau(x), \Phi(x)]\| \in V^{(I)}$$

is required. Now how does this value depend on $\tau(x)$ and $\Phi(x)$? Well, these expressions represent *functions* of x and *all our bound variables* range over D. This leads us to the statement that

$$\|\$\| \in (V^{(I)})U, \text{ where } U = (V^{(I))D}) \times (2^I)^D.$$

because $(V^{(I)})^D$ is the set of all concept-valued functions and $(2^I)^D$ is the set of all propositional functions on D. Thus

$$(\$) \qquad \|\$x\,[\tau(x), \Phi(x)]\|_i = \|\$\|\,(f, F)_i,$$

where $f \in (V^{(I)})^D$ and $F \in (2^I)^D$ are defined by:

$$f(a)_i = \|\tau(\bar{a})\|_i$$

and

$$F(a)_i = \|\Phi(\bar{a})\|_i, \quad \text{for all } a \in D.$$

It is a little hard to give really dramatic examples of such operators which stand by themselves: usually they are compounded out of other, simpler operators. For example

$$\mathrm{I}y\,\forall x\,\Box\,[\Phi(x) \rightarrow y = \tau(x)]$$

would be a likely compound. (Do not ask for a poetic reading of that descriptive phrase, please). It might be possible to always reduce an operator to a compound where the only variable bindings came in the quantifiers and descriptions; but then again maybe not. The matter bears some further thought. Note that in case \$ were a formula maker, the only change would be to make its values propositional concepts.

To emphasize again the kind of interchangeability inherent in this logic we have the following as valid:

$$\forall x \,\Box \tau(x) = \tau'(x) \wedge \forall x \,\Box [\Phi(x) \leftrightarrow \Phi'(x)] \rightarrow \\ \$x\, [\tau(x), \Phi(x)] = \$x\, [\tau'(x), \Phi'(x)].$$

And at risk of repetition, let it be noted that $\Box$ is the *only* modal operator that is suitable for this purpose: that is one of the main reasons for including it among the *logical* constants.

An important consideration that has been neglected up to this point concerns the use of various interpretations. Indeed we have not actually said what an interpretation *is*. This must be remedied at once. An *interpretation* assigns values to the symbols according to their logical types. To specify an interpretation one must first specify V, D, I, and the A_i for $i \in I$. Next for each symbol \$ one must specify its value. What are the symbols? Well at a minimum they are the $\bar{a}$ for $a \in V$; the $\neg$, $\rightarrow$, $\forall$, I, $=$; the special $\tilde{A}$; the $\Box$; and finally all the non-logical symbols \$ which include all the terms and formula makers, with and without bound variables, in whatever number we choose. The first listed are logical (at least they are logical with respect to the given domains of virtual, possible, actual individuals and the indices.) The remainder are non-logical. The values of the logical symbols are *fixed*; the values of the non-logical symbols are open to *variation*. So far I have *not* indicated this freedom in my notation. Let us then call the given interpretation $\mathfrak{A}$ (a German capital A). It is some God-awful multi-tuple, which has hidden in it all the information about the domains, indices, and non-logical symbols. Once we know $\mathfrak{A}$ we know everything. All our semantical rules (like ($\forall$), ($=$), ($\Box$), (\$)) are energized and we can find the value of any well-formed expression (without free variables). The notation I would use is:

$$\|\tau\|^{\mathfrak{A}} \quad \text{and} \quad \|\Phi\|^{\mathfrak{A}},$$

whereas Montague has recommended:

$$\tau_{\mathfrak{A}} \quad \text{and} \quad \Phi_{\mathfrak{A}}.$$

His is shorter – too short it seems to me. The notation leaves us nothing to write when mention of $\mathfrak{A}$ is suppressed. (Of course to some, suppression is evil, and they would never consider doing it.) Thus I prefer the writing of the double bars as forcing me to remember the distinction between the *expression* and its *value*. That clearly is the kind of advice that one can either take or leave: all I ask it that you be reasonably clear about what you are doing. I only hope I have made the *content* of the present approach definite enough.

Having admitted the variability of interpretations, the definition of *logical validity* becomes more definite. Let us state it for *formulas* $\Phi(x, y, \ldots)$ with *free* variables. Such a formula is *valid* if and only if for all interpretations $\mathfrak{A}$ and all individuals $a, b, \ldots \in D$ (the possible individuals of $\mathfrak{A}$) we have

$$\|\Phi(\bar{a}, \bar{b}, \ldots)\|_i^{\mathfrak{A}} = 1$$

for all $i \in I$ (the index set of $\mathfrak{A}$). Since our logic has been first-order logic (only bound individual variables) it will be no surprise to hear that the valid formulas are axiomatizable. The axioms and rules are in fact well-known: predicate logic with an S5 modal logic for $\Box$; in addition the axiom schema of replacement of *necessary* equalities (and biconditionals) is required. David Kaplan and I will present his completeness proof (a standard type of Henkin argument) in our joint paper devoted to the more technical details. Thomason has also made a detailed study of the completeness proofs in the paper he read here at Irvine. His systems are, however, only fragments of the general system described in this paper – though the methods he developed will apply. One bit of advice seems needed at this juncture: the aim of logic is not solely to provide completeness proofs. The real aim is conceptual clarification. Completeness proofs are needed but are not ends in themselves.

One small point concerning the proper formalizations can be mentioned here. It will be noted in the definition of logical validity that the free variables were replaced by constants for elements $a \in D$ and *not* $a \in V$. The reason being that individual variables are for the individuals over which one quantifies. The Greek letters τ, σ, ... in the *metalanguage* are the ones that can be replaced by expressions for virtual entities. In foundational studies I advise *not* making the individual variables do double duty. (For pedagogical purposes I found that the double use *is* better because students dislike too heavy use of Greek letters!)

The next step is to push on to the higher-type logic. For the present

I can only refer to the latest papers of Montague for a discussion. It is interesting to note that in his Helsinki lecture Lemmon discussed modal set theory *without* giving semantics. That can now possibly be done, but I have not worked out the details in full.

VI. INCIDENCE VS. EQUALITY

We have already been led to the distinction between equality and identity. It took me a very long time to understand what was involved inasmuch as I was confused about a *weaker* relation I shall write as

$$\tau \approx \sigma$$

and call *incidence*. I was pleased (in a sense) to find that the same confusion has been the crux, at least in my opinion, of the recent interchanges between Hintikka and Føllesdal. It would seem to be finally the proper time to clear up the distinction through the use of the semantics advocated here. In fact, I feel that the present approach is better suited to providing the needed clarification than are Hintikka's model sets – though he can claim other advantages for his method. The point is that we must clearly distinguish between individuals and individual concepts – which our semantics does. I do not feel that the situation is as transparent with Hintikka, but maybe it can be made so. I am completely indebted to Montague and Kaplan for showing me the way to the present formulations.

The idea intuitively is that two individuals that are generally distinct might share all the same properties (of a certain kind!) with respect to the present world (present index). Hence they are equivalent or *incident* at the moment. Relative to other points of reference they may cease to be incident. This will allow for branching and merging of individuals – at least as far as distinctions concerned with certain kinds of properties permit. My feeling is that the confusion about merging of individuals rests on this question of the *allowed properties*: if the class of properties is vague and changeable, then the equivalence of individuals will seem paradoxial. We have to agree to a class of properties given in advance – or at least agree that the notion is relative to a fixed class of properties that we wish to investigate more closely. I am reasonably certain that this is what Hintikka has in mind. Unfortunately he uses the equality symbol = for this incidence relation, which leads to unnecessary arguments when others read $=$ in a different way. We shall see why it is tempting to use $=$ in this way in a moment.

How can we represent the idea of incidence in our semantics? We could of course add a non-logical constant $\approx$ and the axioms of an equivalence relation. This is unsatisfactory because no particular analysis is involved. A better approach is the specialization of the class of models (interpretations) to those with a more defined structure, the features of which can be interpreted in an intuitive and suggestive way. So we begin by supposing that to each individual $a \in V$ and relative to each $i \in I$ we can attach certain *particulars* that specify or individuate a with respect to the properties involved. We take these particulars as forming some kind of abstract object, call it the *state* of a at i, and for convenience let S be a set having all these states of all the individuals as members. *Now this next step may be an oversimplification*: we then IDENTIFY the individual a with this individuating function. Thus we make $V \subseteq S^I$, and for each $a \in V$ and $i \in I$ write a_i for the state of a at i. The meaning of incidence is now determined:

$$(\approx_\circ) \qquad \|\bar{a} \approx \bar{b}\|_i = 1 \quad \text{iff} \quad a_i = b_i .$$

(I have written $\approx_\circ$ because this clause involves only individual constants; the full version for compound terms will be given later.)

It is seen that we are assuming that, to know an individual, it is sufficient to know all particulars about him from all points of reference. In words that does not sound too bad, but it is an assumption that there are *enough* points of reference and sufficiently detailed particulars. I can imagine in later development that we may drop this condition; but for present purpose of trying to see how a coherent incidence relation can be introduced, the convention does not seem too unreasonable.

Note that equality of individuals, under our convention, can be defined in terms of incidence because the following is now valid:

$$\bar{a} = \bar{b} \leftrightarrow \Box \bar{a} \approx \bar{b}$$

It is this feature that undoubtedly led Hintikka to take $\approx$ as more fundamental than what I write as $=$. The relationship between the two notions is somewhat obscured by Hintikka, however, because he uses an operator $\boxed{\rho}$ instead of the stronger $\Box$, and this introduces some complications. In any case, I want to argue now that no matter how the modalities are treated we *cannot* take $\approx$ and define $=$.

The trouble comes in with the individual concepts. I hope that I have finally made this distinction between individuals and individual concepts clear to everyone. At least for me it was the semantic approach and the suggestions of Montague and Kaplan that made the clarity possible. You see, even if we treat individuals as *functions* in S^I, the concepts enter in a secondary way (on top of the individuals, as it were) and have values which are functions with the *individuals* as values. It seems to me now that this is really the only proper arrangement. Thus for a term τ we will find that

$$\|\tau\| \in (S^I)^{(I)}.$$

(The value of a term, remember, is a *partial* function. It seems better to take the $a \in V$ as *total* functions $a \in S^I$, because an individual can always be given *some* abstract entity as its state no matter which $i \in I$ is chosen.) This requires the following semantics:

$$\|\tau \approx \sigma\|_i = 1 \quad \text{iff} \quad (\|\tau\|_i)_i = (\|\sigma\|_i)_i .$$

That is, find out which individuals τ and σ denote ($\|\tau\|_i$ and $\|\sigma\|_i$), and *then* see if they have the same state. Everything is fine (i.e. the truth value is well-determined) if both $\|\tau\|_i$ and $\|\sigma\|_i$ are defined; otherwise our convention for *truth* is that they *both* be undefined.

Now for the trouble: what does $\tau \approx \sigma$ mean in general? Formally we have:

$$\|\Box\tau \approx \sigma\|_i = 1 \quad \text{iff} \quad (\|\tau\|_j)_j = (\|\sigma\|_j)_j \quad \text{all} \quad j \in I .$$

Clearly this is *not* the same as $\|\tau\| = \|\sigma\|$ *unless* $\|\tau\|$ and $\|\sigma\|$ are *constant* functions in $V^{(I)}$. Let us try a homely example: take τ to be 'the President of the United States' and σ to be 'the biggest crook in the world'. (In our interpretation any similarity to persons living or dead is purely coincidental.) For simplicity we assume I to involve *time*. Thus for each $i \in I$, the individual $\|\tau\|_i$ is the (whole) person who is President at time *i*. If we like we can think of $(\|\tau\|_i)_i$ as an instantaneous portrait of the man which captures on very sensitive paper his essential qualities at time *i*. As *i* varies in *I* we run through the (rather extensive) official portrait gallery dedicated to the office of president. Meanwhile the FBI, acting quite on its own, has been photographing at each instant the biggest crook of the moment. One can imagine the consternation when a comparison reveals the truth of $\Box\tau \approx \sigma$. One can charitably excuse the President himself, however, for it is only by virtue of his high office that he must be put in that other distasteful category. The statement $\Box\tau \approx \sigma$, though unpleasant, is perfectly meaningful and does not entail $\tau = \sigma$.

Why does not it? As I write the above I notice a certain weakness of argument. Thinking of I as simple time may not be enough. Our elementary view of individuals is such that if $a_i = b_i$ at *one* time i, then $a = b$ (all times!). We have to consider not only of the flow of time but also of *alternative* courses of events. – No, come to think of it, that is not the answer either, for that only makes the individual concept $\|\tau\|$ fatter but not more amusing. – Or maybe it does. (Oh my, I see that much more thought and experimentation are needed to make the ideas into something useful. In any case I feel that a precise and general semantical framework is essential, and that is, as I have been trying to indicate, now available.) Let us attempt to save this example. We can imagine as a possible individual the stirling public servant, possessor of mountains of good qualities from every point of reference. Next imagine a master crook. These are not individual concepts but possible individuals – distinct individuals. The public servant is not always president; the crook is not always successful. But at that moment of triumph when both reach the high points of their careers we find that they are the same in all particulars.

No, it just will not do. I am twisting the language to fit an abstractly constructed semantics! Nevertheless I still think that the relation $\approx$ has a sensible meaning. The trouble is that I have been trying to defend the principle:

$$\bar{a} = \bar{b} \leftrightarrow \Box \bar{a} \approx \bar{b},$$

and the defense has gone wrong as I have tried to write it down. It seems to me that one must read $\bar{a} \approx \bar{b}$ as '$\bar{a}$ and $\bar{b}$ are equivalent (indistinguishable) with respect to certain (fixed) properties'. Indeed, as Hintikka has pointed out, there may be several different ways of individuating our individuals (different perceptions) which would provide for several equivalence relations $\approx_1, \approx_2, \ldots, \approx_n$, in my framework. Whether any of these should satisfy the above biconditional is a moot point. But let me again stress that we must take care not to confuse equivalence and equality. We must, on my view, make the distinctions which can be summarized in the following diagrams where the arrows indicate implications. Note that the diagrams are *different* for individuals and individual concepts. The biconditionals are all firmly justified; the single arrows are clearly not reversible – except for the questionable - - →. I guess we will come to reject that also.

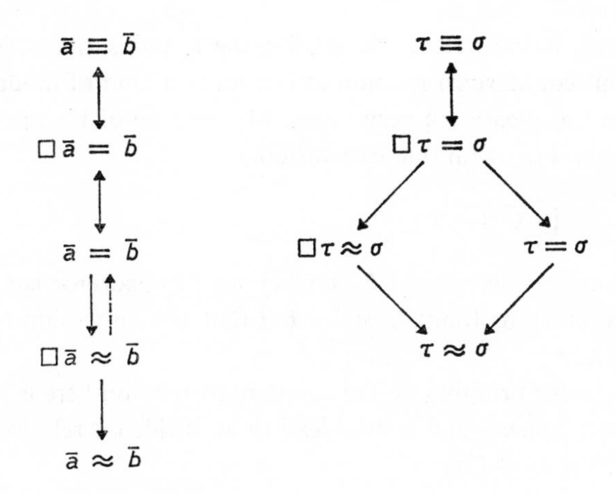

The puzzle of cross indentifications of individuals has been treated by David Lewis from another point of view. He thinks of

$$D = \bigcup_{i \in I} A_i$$

and of the A_i's as being disjoint:

$$A_i \cap A_j = 0 \quad \text{for} \quad i \neq j.$$

That is, each world $i \in I$ has its own separate set of tokens representing individuals. Having made the individuals separate, we now join some of them together again by the *counterpart* relation C. If $a \in A_i$ and $b \in A_j$, then aCb means that a is the *counterpart* of b in A_i: the person b would be if he lived in A_i, or at least one who is very much like him – we will allow for several. In case $i = j$, we agree that the reading of the relationship demands $a = b$.

We can easily put Lewis' relation into our language by using the constant $\bar{C}$ as with our previous notation. These principles will then be satisfied:

$$\forall x, y\,[x\,\bar{C}\,y \rightarrow \tilde{A}x],$$
$$\forall x, y\,[x\,\bar{C}\,y \wedge \tilde{A}y \rightarrow x = y],$$
$$\forall x\,[\tilde{A}x \rightarrow x\,\bar{C}\,x].$$

(If one wants, he can rewrite these using the $\forall.$ and $\exists.$ quantifiers.) Lewis then uses his counterpart relation to introduce a kind of modal operator which does not please me very much. My reading of his operator gives for a formula $\Phi(x)$ with one free variable:

$$\forall y\,[y\,\bar{C}\,x \rightarrow \Phi(y)]$$

for the meaning of *necessarily* $\Phi(x)$. I feel that this operator is too complicated to be taken as fundamental – but that is a discussion for another time and place.

The reason for bringing up the counterpart relation here is that it does have intuitive appeal, and it does lead to an incidence relation that may be natural. Let us define

$$\tau \approx \sigma \leftrightarrow \forall.x\,[x\,\bar{C}\,\tau \leftrightarrow x\,\bar{C}\,\sigma]$$

We then find that:

$$\forall x, y\,[\tilde{A}x \wedge x \approx y \rightarrow x\,\bar{C}\,y],$$

though the converse does not hold in general. Thus the incidence relation is too weak to be used to define counterparts, but it does have a very close connection with them. We can read $\bar{a} \approx \bar{b}$ as saying that $\bar{a}$ and $\bar{b}$ have the same counterparts in the current world, which means that they will have a large number of properties in common.

To summarize the foregoing rather unsatisfactory discussion we can make these points: (1) *at least three relations* $\approx$, $=$, $\equiv$ (which are easily confused) *do arise naturally*; (2) *semantical discussions are available that make the distinctions precise*; (3) *one needs to keep in mind that individual concepts behave differently from individuals*. Though David Kaplan has spoken at length on these distinction in several public lectures, I find in rereading his notes that I am not really convinced that we have a final solution to cross-world identifications. But I do have some advise to give (surprise!): we need to make more experiments on the construction of models. Up to this point our indices of possible worlds have been too vague, too abstract. The idea of using $V \subseteq S^I$ was to treat an individual as a *process* (in the mathematical sense of the word.) That is, an analysis of the individual must be attempted. The method is not yet discredited, because it has not really been carried out in sufficient detail. Just to write S^I is only to indicate a skeleton but not to give it any flesh. One essential step to take in this analysis is to make the elements more specific. That must be done first before we can decide what to put in S. I do not feel that Hintikka's method of model sets would give the right solution, because I feel that one must have a concept of the *kind* of possible worlds there are *before* one can specify what is true about them. Well, that is a very philosophical question, and it would seem best discussed after one has tried to construct interesting models within the framework of this semantics. My advice is to work on this problem.

Princeton University

POSTSCRIPT (DECEMBER, 1969)

This paper was written very hastily in the latter part of May, 1968. The haste is apparent and the style intolerable; I find it now very painful reading. The point of writing the essay was to stimulate discussion, but only two of my colleagues took the time to respond (to me) in writing: Kaplan and Montague. Their detailed criticisms showed me that the paper should be completely rewritten – a task which I have unfortunately not had the time to undertake. Nevertheless the editor was kind enough to encourage publication in this very imperfect form. I would like to thank him for this and hope the obvious flaws will provoke others to do a better job.

Though I was only able to take account of a few of the many points made to me by Kaplan and Montague it will be helpful to quote some of their remarks so that my paper will not make entirely the wrong impression. First from a letter by David Kaplan (July 28, 1968):

I am repelled by your calling $\equiv$ 'identity'. This stems, I believe, from a rejection of what Carnap calls 'the method of the relation' [see Meaning & Necessity] and the attendant talk of denotation. There are just these two entities associated with each term: an extension and an intension. $=$ indicates same extension and $\equiv$ indicates same intension. But this is to ignore the primacy of extensional contexts. It is technically more convenient to treat all constants as intensional simply because we can represent the extensional ones as a subset. But one of the main aims of doing intensional logic in the way we do it is to describe intensional object languages in extensional metalanguages. If one is overly impressed by the simplifications that come from treating all constants as (at most) intensional, they may even start thinking of the intension as a kind of denotatum and talk, as you do at places, of the principles of intensional interchange as supplying a degree of 'extensionality' to the language. Look at the values of the variables to find the individuals and then keep individuals and individual concepts forever distinct. Although it is in a technical sense correct to say that extensional logic is a special case of the more general intensional logic, it is also in an important sense correct to say that extensional logic can be taken as the most general form. That is, that we can keep the sense and denotation distinction (or the name relation) between *what* we are talking about and *how* we talk about it. It was this that Frege saw and Church assumed. I suppose the situation here is very much like the question of the primacy of two valued logic and can be argued on both sides. The important thing is to be clear; I don't think it helps to call $\equiv$ 'identity' or to pretend that the displayed formulas on p. 121 are like Leibniz' law.

Concerning incidence, Kaplan had written to me earlier (July 10, 1968):

It appears that around page 132 you lost track of some entities. I think there are two problems here. (1) can $=$ be defined using $\approx$?, (2) can $\tau = \sigma$ be defined by $\Box(\tau \approx \sigma)$? The answer to (1) is yes but only if there is no merging of individuals. So in your example of people through time (where, as you remark, merging is implausible) we can use the definition:

$$\tau = \sigma \leftrightarrow \tau \approx \sigma$$

But of course if merging is allowed, as for highways through space this definition won't work, since $\overline{\text{U.S. 60}} \approx \overline{\text{U.S. 70}}$ is true at West Covina but $\overline{\text{U.S. 60}} = \overline{\text{U.S. 70}}$ is false everywhere. (Here we can even use *essential* names of the highways, $\overline{\text{U.S. 60}}$ names U.S. 60 everywhere.)

The answer to (2) is always NO. And your example shows that $\Box(\tau \approx \sigma)$ is not necessary for $\tau = \sigma$. To put it another way $\tau = \sigma$ does not imply $\Box(\tau \approx \sigma)$. For suppose that at the moment The President $=$ The Crook, then the gallery representing the office of the President and the FBI gallery will share a picture: namely that of the current office holder. But if in olden days presidents were more honest, the two galleries will disagree at many points and so $\Box$(The President $\approx$ The Crook) will be false.

To show that $\Box(\tau \approx \sigma)$ is not sufficient, we must of course again assume the possibility of merging and dividing (otherwise $[\Box(\tau \approx \sigma) \rightarrow \tau \approx \sigma]$ and $[\tau \approx \sigma \leftrightarrow \tau = \sigma]$). Did you know that the soon to be built Federal highway 0 will be, for its whole length, a 73 lane road? (It will run through the center of all major cities; the idea was conceived in Los Angeles.) Being built with joint Federal State funds the Highway will coincide at every point with one of the state highways which will of course widen to 73 lanes where it joins Fed. 0 and then narrow down again when it separates. Our points of reference are the major cities, in each city it is true that: *The State highway with 73 lanes* $\approx$ $\overline{\textit{Fed. 0}}$, so $\Box$ (*The State highway with 73 lanes* $\approx$ $\overline{\textit{Fed. 0}}$) is also true. But it is nowhere true that *The State highway with 73 lanes* $=$ $\overline{\textit{Fed. 0}}$, since all State highways veer off somewhere (and besides, don't run beyond the state borders).

To defend the principle on your page 132. From left to right we have $\tau = \sigma \rightarrow \tau \approx \sigma$ is valid so $\Box(\tau = \sigma) \rightarrow \Box(\tau \approx \sigma)$, and as you point out earlier we have $\bar{a} = \bar{b} \rightarrow \Box(\bar{a} = \bar{b})$. From right to left: $\Box(\bar{a} \approx \bar{b})$ says that for all $i \in I$, $(\|\bar{a}\|_i)_i = (\|\bar{b}\|_i)_i$. But by definition for all $i \in I$, $\|\bar{a}\|_i = a$, so we have for all $i \in I$, $a_i = b_i$. Now a and b *are* just functions with domain I, so $a = b$.

Montague makes one of these points in a different way (June 30, 1968):

You raise the question of the intuitive meaning of $\Box(\sigma \approx \tau)$. Your example, of 'the President' & 'the biggest crook', is unfortunate, because both terms denote humans, and hence continuants which (as you noticed) are identical if ever incident. But let's try $\sigma =$ 'the President' & $\tau =$ 'the heap of molecules in the President's chair'. Then $\sigma \neq \tau$ is true, because no organism is a heap of molecules; indeed, the equality fails not only at present but at all times: $\Box(\sigma \neq \tau)$ is true. But suppose that the president (and nothing else) is now occupying the president's chair. Then $\sigma \approx \tau$ is true. If we also suppose that the presidency is so engrossing that at every time i, the President at time i (and nothing else) occupies the President's chair (so that each president sits at his desk continuously from the moment he is sworn in till the moment he leaves office), then $\Box(\sigma \approx \tau)$ is true. Thus $\Box(\sigma \approx \tau)$ is compatible not only with $\sigma \neq \tau$, but even with $\Box(\sigma \neq \tau)$. (It's of course easy to construct examples in which we have $[\sigma = \tau \wedge \neg \Box (\sigma \approx \tau)]$; but as you observe we cannot have $[\sigma = \tau \wedge \Box \neg (\sigma \approx \tau)]$ or $[\Box(\sigma = \tau) \wedge \neg \Box(\sigma \approx \tau)]$.)

Further Montague objects strongly to my interpretation of predicate constants and feels that preservation of validity under substitution of formulas for predicates is an 'empty dogma'. And he has good grounds for this view. He goes on to say:

Thus I remain unregenerately convinced that the natural systems are, in order of increasing strength: (1) strict modal logic, which is the 1*st* order part, containing only individual terms and the logical operator $\Box$, of the system I have sketched (this is essentially the system of Kripke-Cocchiarella-Thomason); (2) pragmatics, which adds arbitrary nonlogical propositional operators (of 1 or more places, but binding 0 var's), on the interpretation of which we agree; (3) extended pragmatics, which contains arbitrary variable-binding operators but in connection with which there is some latitude as to which kinds of operators shall be taken as basic; (4) the 2*nd* order system I have sketched for you; (5) higher order systems built up on that pattern.

He then concludes that my system as amended with regards predicate constants, or where "predicate constants are (as a technical simplification) discarded and general variable-binders (more general than yours) used instead", could be regarded as a variant of his extended pragmatics. I am sorry not to be able to summarize his systems and arguments here (nor the subsequent correspondence between Kaplan and Montague) but can only refer the reader to the several recent papers where Montague explains his approach to intensional logic.

INDEX OF NAMES

SYNTHESE LIBRARY

Monographs on Epistemology, Logic, Methodology,
Philosophy of Science, Sociology of Science and of Knowledge, and on the
Mathematical Methods of Social and Behavioral Sciences

P. V. TAVANEC (ed.), *Problems of the Logic of Scientific Knowledge*. 1969, XII + 429 pp. Dfl. 95.—

‡ROBERT S. COHEN and RAYMOND J. SEEGER (eds.), *Boston Studies in the Philosophy of Science*. Volume VI: *Ernst Mach: Physicist and Philosopher*. 1970, VIII + 295 pp. Dfl. 38.—

‡MARSHALL SWAIN (ed.), *Induction, Acceptance, and Rational Belief*. 1970, VII + 232 pp. Dfl. 40.—

‡NICHOLAS RESCHER *et al.*, (eds.), *Essays in Honor of Carl G. Hempel. A Tribute on the Occasion of his Sixty-Fifth Birthday*. 1969, VII + 272 pp. Dfl. 46.—

‡PATRICK SUPPES, *Studies in the Methodology and Foundations of Science. Selected Papers from 1951 to 1969*. 1969, XII + 473 pp. Dfl. 72.—

‡JAAKKO HINTIKKA, *Models for Modalities. Selected Essays*. 1969, IX + 220 pp. Dfl. 34.—

‡D. DAVIDSON and J. HINTIKKA: (eds.), *Words and Objections: Essays on the Work of W. V. Quine*. 1969, VIII + 366 pp. Dfl. 48.—

‡J. W. DAVIS, D. J. HOCKNEY, and W. K. WILSON (eds.), *Philosophical Logic*. 1969, VIII + 277 pp. Dfl. 45.—

‡ROBERT S. COHEN and MARX W. WARTOFSKY (eds.), *Boston Studies in the Philosophy of Science*. Volume V: *Proceedings of the Boston Colloquium for the Philosophy of Science 1966/1968*. 1969, VIII + 482 pp. Dfl. 58.—

‡ROBERT S. COHEN and MARX W. WARTOFSKY (eds.), *Boston Studies in the Philosophy of Science*. Volume IV: *Proceedings of the Boston Colloquium for the Philosophy of Science 1966/1968*. 1969, VIII + 537 pp. Dfl. 69.—

‡NICHOLAS RESCHER, *Topics in Philosophical Logic*. 1968, XIV + 347 pp. Dfl. 62.—

p.t.o.

‡GÜNTHER PATZIG, *Aristotle's Theory of the Syllogism. A Logical-Philological Study of Book A of the Prior Analytics*. 1968, XVII + 215 pp. Dfl. 45.—

‡C. D. BROAD, *Induction, Probability, and Causation. Selected Papers*. 1968, XI + 296 pp. Dfl. 48.—

‡ROBERT S. COHEN and MARX W. WARTOFSKY (eds.), *Boston Studies in the Philosophy of Science*. Volume III: *Proceedings of the Boston Colloquium for the Philosophy of Science 1964/1966*. 1967, XLIX + 489 pp. Dfl. 65.—

‡GUIDO KÜNG, *Ontology and the Logistic Analysis of Language. An Enquiry into the Contemporary Views on Universals*. 1967, XI + 210 pp. Dfl. 34.—

*EVERT W. BETH and JEAN PIAGET, *Mathematical Epistemology and Psychology*. 1966. XXII + 326 pp. Dfl. 54.—

*EVERT W. BETH, *Mathematical Thought. An Introduction to the Philosophy of Mathematics*. 1965, XII + 208 pp. Dfl. 30.—

‡PAUL LORENZEN, *Formal Logic*. 1965, VIII + 123 pp. Dfl. 18.75

‡GEORGES GURVITCH, *The Spectrum of Social Time*. 1964, XXVI + 152 pp. Dfl. 20.—

‡A. A. ZINOV'EV, *Philosophical Problems of Many-Valued Logic*. 1963, XIV + 155 pp. Dfl. 23.—

‡MARX W. WARTOFSKY (ed.), *Boston Studies in the Philosophy of Science*. Volume I: *Proceedings of the Boston Colloquium for Philosophy of Science, 1961–1962*. 1963, VII + 212 pp. Dfl. 22.50

‡B. H. KAZEMIER and D. VUYSJE (eds.), *Logic and Language. Studies dedicated to Professor Rudolf Carnap on the Occasion of his Seventieth Birthday*. 1962, VI + 246 pp. Dfl. 24.50

*EVERT W. BETH, *Formal Methods. An Introduction to Symbolic Logic and to the Study of Effective Operations in Arithmetic and Logic*. 1962, XIV + 170 pp. Dfl. 23.50

*HANS FREUDENTHAL (ed.), *The Concept and the Role of the Model in Mathematics and Natural and Social Sciences. Proceedings of a Colloquium held at Utrecht, The Netherlands, January 1960*. 1961, VI + 194 pp. Dfl. 21.—

‡P. L. R. GUIRAUD, *Problèmes et méthodes de la statistique linguistique*. 1960, VI + 146 pp. Dfl. 15.75

*J. M. BOCHEŃSKI, *A Precis of Mathematical Logic*. 1959, X + 100 pp. Dfl. 15.75

Sole Distributors in the U.S.A. and Canada:

*GORDON & BREACH, INC., 150 Fifth Avenue, New York, N.Y. 10011
‡HUMANITIES PRESS, INC., 303 Park Avenue South, New York, N.Y. 10010